ICSA Publishing

Published by ICSA Publishing Limited
16 Park Crescent
London W1N 4AH

Typeset in 10/12.5 pt Meridien with Frutiger Light
By Fakenham Photosetting Ltd, Fakenham, Norfolk

Printed and bound in Great Britain by
T J International Ltd, Padstow, Cornwall

British Library Cataloguing in Publication Data

A catalogue record for this book is available from the British Library

ISBN: 1–86072–119–2

Acknowledgement

Figures 2, 3, 4, 5, 8, 10, 11, 14, 15 and 16 are Crown copyright. Crown copyright material is reproduced with the permission of the Controller of Her Majesty's Stationery Office.

Contents

List of abbreviations

AC	Appeal Cases
ACOP	Approved Code of Practice
AER	*All England Reports*
BS	British Standard
CBI	Confederation of British Industry
CDMR	Construction (Design and Management) Regulations 1994
CHSWR	Construction (Health, Safety and Welfare) Regulations 1996
COSHHR	Control of Substances Hazardous to Health Regulations 1999
DSE	Display screen equipment
EMAS	Employment Medical Advisory Service
FPA	Fire Precautions Act 1971
HRA	Human Reliability Assessment
HSC	Health and Safety Commission
HSE	Health and Safety Executive
HSWA	Health and Safety at Work etc. Act 1974
IEE	Institute of Electrical Engineers
LOLER	Lifting Operations and Lifting Equipment Regulations 1998
LT	*Law Times Reports*
MEL	Maximum exposure limit
MHOR	Manual Handling Operations Regulations 1992
MHSWR	Management of Health and Safety at Work Regulations 1999
OES	Occupational exposure standard
PPE	Personal protective equipment
PPEWR	Personal Protective Equipment at Work Regulations 1992
PUWER	Provision and Use of Work Equipment Regulations 1998
Reg.	Regulation
RIDDOR	Reporting of Injuries, Diseases and Dangerous Occurrences Regulations 1995
RoSPA	Royal Society for the Prevention of Accidents
RPE	Respiratory protective equipment
RSI	Repetitive strain injury
VDU	Visual display unit
VWF	Vibration-induced white finger
WHSWR	Workplace (Health, Safety and Welfare) Regulations 1992

Preface

The health and safety of employees and, indeed, other people who may be affected by work activities, is a matter no employer can afford to ignore.

Penalties imposed in both the criminal and civil courts can be extensive when people are killed or injured at work, or if they suffer diseases associated with work activities.

Furthermore, the last decade has seen considerable developments in health and safety law, as a result of which the room for manoeuvre on the part of employers has been greatly reduced. In particular, the Management of Health and Safety at Work Regulations 1992, followed by the extended version in 2000, completely changed the face of the law bringing in strict duties on employers with regard to risk assessment, the installation of health and safety management systems, the appointment of competent persons and the provision of health and safety training, together with specific provisions for pregnant workers and young persons. All other recent legislation must be read in conjunction with these general duties imposed under the Management of Health and Safety at Work Regulations.

Managers need to be aware of a number of specific health and safety issues which affect any business or undertaking. This book has been written in readily accessible topic form to provide guidance on these important issues.

Jeremy Stranks
June 2000

Accidents and injuries

Introduction

An accident can be defined as 'a deviation from the normal, the expected or the planned, usually resulting in injury'.

The majority of accidents result in some form of injury and, in certain cases, death. In addition to the pain and suffering arising from accidents all accidents represent some form of loss to the organisation in terms of, for example, fines in the criminal courts, claims for negligence, lost production, lost time and damage to plant and equipment. Certain injuries, such as the fracture of an arm or leg, loss of an eye or amputation of a hand, are classed as 'major injuries' under the Reporting of Injuries, Diseases and Dangerous Occurrences Regulations 1995 (RIDDOR). Other injuries, such as cuts and abrasions, may only require first aid treatment. All accidents resulting in injury, however, should be recorded in the Accident Book (BI 510).

Accident investigation

The investigation of the direct and indirect causes of accidents is a reactive strategy in safety management. There are very good reasons, however, for investigating accidents thoroughly and effectively:

1. If the accident is the result of a breach of Statute or Regulations, the injured party may institute civil proceedings against the employer or other persons.
2. The injury may be reportable to the enforcing authority under the Reporting of Injuries, Diseases and Dangerous Occurrences Regulations 1995 (RIDDOR).
3. The accident may result in lost production.
4. A serious accident, particularly a fatal one, can have a long-term detrimental effect on the morale of the workforce and management/worker relations, and on a purely humanitarian basis, no one likes to see people killed or injured.
5. Plant and equipment may need to be repaired or replaced, with possible consequent delays.

6. In most cases, immediate remedial action is necessary in order to prevent a recurrence.

Above all, the purpose of an accident investigation is *not* to apportion blame or fault, although blame or fault may eventually be apportioned as a result of the accident investigation.

Which accidents should be investigated?

All accidents, as well as 'near misses', ought to be investigated. However, as this may be impractical, the following factors should be considered when deciding which accidents to investigate as a priority:

1. the type of accident (e.g. fall from a height, chemical handling, machinery-related);
2. the form and severity of injury, or the potential for serious injury and/or damage;
3. whether the event points to a particular accident trend;
4. the involvement of articles or substances used at work (e.g. machinery, WORK EQUIPMENT, HAZARDOUS SUBSTANCES), and the ensuing damage or loss;
5. the possibility of a breach of the LEGISLATION (e.g. of the Health and Safety at Work etc. Act 1974 (HSWA));
6. whether the injury or occurrence is notifiable and reportable to the enforcing authority; and
7. whether the accident should be reported to the insurance company.

Practical accident investigation

When a serious or fatal accident occurs speed is essential, especially in interviewing injured persons and witnesses. The following procedure is recommended:

1. Establish the facts as quickly and fully as possible with regard to:

   (a) the general environment;
   (b) the plant, machinery, practice or work system involved; and
   (c) the sequence of events leading to the accident.

2. Photograph the scene of the accident *before* any clearing up is done.
3. Draw sketches and take measurements so that a scale drawing can be made.
4. Compile a list of all witnesses and interview them, in the presence of a third party if necessary, and take full statements. (As these statements may be subject to disclosure, it may be prudent to take legal advice before interviewing witnesses.)

5. Evaluate the accuracy, reliability and relevance of the facts and witnesses' versions of the accident. Examine closely any contradictory evidence. Never dismiss a fact that does not fit in with the rest.
6. Endeavour to arrive at conclusions as to what caused the accident on the basis of the relevant facts.
7. Learn fully about the work system involved.
8. Consider the people involved in terms of their age, training, experience and level of supervision, and the nature of the work (e.g. routine, sporadic or incidental).
9. In certain cases, plant and equipment may need to be examined by a specialist (e.g. a consultant engineer).
10. Produce a report for the responsible manager, emphasising the causes and remedies to prevent a recurrence, including any changes necessary. As other people may investigate the accident (e.g. trade unions, insurance companies, lawyers, and enforcing authority) it is essential that any accident report be accurate, comprehensible and identifies the causes.
11. In complex and serious cases, consider the establishment of an investigating committee, comprising managers, supervisors, technical specialists and trade union safety representatives.

The outcome of accident investigation

Feedback on the causes of accidents is essential. An effective investigation should result in one (or more) of the following recommendations:

1. the issuing of instructions by management covering systems of work, the need for more effective guarding of machinery or safe MANUAL HANDLING procedures;
2. the establishment of a working party or committee to undertake further Investigation, perhaps in conjunction with members of the safety committee and/or safety representatives;
3. the preparation and issue of Codes of Practice or Guidance Notes dealing with the procedures necessary to minimise a given risk (e.g. the use of a permit to work system);
4. the identification of training needs for groups of individuals and the implementation of a training programme designed to meet these needs;
5. the formal analysis of the job or system in question, to identify the skill, knowledge and safety components of the job;
6. identification of the need for further information relating to articles and materials used at work (e.g. work equipment, chemical substances);
7. identification of the need for better environmental control (e.g. noise reduction at source, or improved lighting);

8. employee involvement in health and safety issues (e.g. the establishment of a health and safety committee); and
9. identification of the specific responsibilities of groups with regard to safe working practices.

Above all, a system of monitoring should be implemented to ensure that the lessons which have been learned from the accident are implemented or incorporated in future systems of work, and that procedures and operating systems have been produced for all grades of staff.

The cost of accidents and injuries at work

All accidents, whether resulting in personal injury, damage to property or plant, and/or interruption of the business activity, represent a loss to an organisation.

Direct costs

Direct costs (sometimes referred to as insured costs) are largely concerned with an organisation's liabilities as an employer and occupier of premises. Direct costs are covered by premiums paid to an insurance company to provide cover against claims made by an injured party. Claims by insured persons and users of products manufactured by the company, which are settled either in or out of court, together with fines imposed by a court for breaches of health and safety legislation, are also included in direct costs. Substantial legal defence costs may also be incorporated in this category.

Indirect costs

Indirect costs are many and varied and are often difficult to predict. Some may be included, and thus hidden, in other costs, e.g. labour, production or administration costs. Indirect costs are often ignored for this reason. Some are simple to quantify, however, and include the following:

1. *Treatment costs:* First aid, transport to hospital, hospital charges, other costs, e.g. local doctor, consultants.
2. *Lost time costs:* Lost time of injured person, supervisor, first aiders and others involved.
3. *Production costs:* Lost production, extra staff payments to meet production targets, damage to plant, vehicles, raw materials and finished products.
4. *Training and supervision costs:* Training for replacement and existing labour force, extra supervision costs.
5. *Investigation costs:* Many people may be involved in the investigation of

	£	p
Date Time Place of accident		
Details of Accident		
Injured person		
Name in full		
Address		
Occupation		
Length of service		
Injury details		
Accident costs		
Direct costs		
1. % occupier's liability premium		
2. % increased premiums payable		
3. Claims		
4. Fines and damages awarded in court		
5. Court and legal representation cost		
Indirect costs		
6. Treatment First aid		
Transport		
Hospital		
Others		
7. Lost time Injured person		
Management		
Supervisors		
First aiders		
Others		
8. Lost production Overtime payments		
Damage to plant, vehicles, etc.		
Training/supervision replacement labour		
9. Investigation Management		
Safety adviser		
Others, e.g. safety representatives		
Liaison with enforcement authority		
10. Other costs Replacement of personal items:		
injured person		
others		
Other miscellaneous costs		
TOTAL COSTS		

Figure 1 Accident costs assessment

5

an accident or incident. Investigation costs should be based on the total hours involved by all concerned.

6. *Miscellaneous costs:* Ex gratia payments, replacement costs of personal items, incidental costs incurred by witnesses, etc.

7. *Costs to the injured person:* Loss of earnings, loss of total earning capacity, legal costs in pursuing injury claim, possible legal costs in defending a prosecution for 'unsafe behaviour' at work. (See Figure 1.)

The use of accident data

Various forms of accident data are compiled by organisations and a number of standard indices are used, e.g. accident incident rate, frequency rate, severity rate and duration rate. Whilst such calculations have a purpose in indicating accident trends, they are unreliable as a measure of performance.

The crucial point is that counting accidents provides incomplete, untimely and possibly misleading answers to the questions: Are we implementing our safety plan fully? And, is it the right plan?

See also REPORTING AND RECORDING.

Introduction

Organisations that successfully manage health and safety give health and safety advisers status and ensure they have the competence to advise management and workers with authority and independence. Subjects on which they advise include:

1. health and safety policy formulation and development;
2. safety promotion in all parts of the organisation (including the supporting systems) in order to develop a positive health and safety culture and to secure the effective implementation of policy;
3. planning for health and safety, including the setting of realistic short- and long-term objectives, deciding priorities and establishing adequate performance standards;
4. day-to-day implementation and monitoring of policy and plans, including accident and incident investigation, reporting and analysis; and
5. reviewing performance and auditing the whole safety management system.

The role of advisers

To fulfil their functions, advisers have to:

1. maintain adequate information systems on relevant LEGISLATION (civil and criminal) and on guidance and developments in general and safety management practice;
2. be able to interpret the law and understand how it applies to the organisation;
3. establish and keep up-to-date organisational and risk control standards;
4. establish and maintain procedures for the REPORTING, investigating and RECORDING and analysis of ACCIDENTS and incidents;
5. establish and maintain adequate and appropriate MONITORING and auditing systems; and
6. present themselves and their advice in an independent and effective manner.

Relationships of health and safety advisers within the organisation

The position of health and safety advisers in the organisation is such that they support the provision of authoritative and independent advice. The post-holder has a direct reporting line to directors on matters of policy and authority to stop work which is being carried out in contravention of agreed standards and which puts people at risk of injury. Health and safety advisers have a responsibility for professional standards and systems, and on a large site or in a group of companies may also have line management responsibilities for junior health and safety professionals.

Outside the organisation

Health and safety advisers are involved in liaison with a wide range of outside bodies and individuals, including local authority environmental health officers and licensing officials, architects and consultants, etc., the fire service, contractors, insurance companies, clients and customers, the Health and Safety Executive (HSE), the public, equipment suppliers, HM Coroner, or in Scotland the Procurator Fiscal, the media, the police, general practitioners and hospital staff.

Commercial premises

Introduction

Commercial premises are not considered to be dangerous places compared, say, with factories or construction sites. However, every year a large number of people sustain injuries or become ill as a result of accidents and poor working conditions in offices. The principal legal requirements relating to commercial premises are covered in the Fire Precautions Act 1971 (FPA), the Fire Precautions (Workplaces) Regulations 1997 and the Health and Safety at Work etc. Act 1974 (HSWA).

Principal hazards in commercial premises

FIRE is perhaps the greatest hazard. However, a substantial number of accidents are associated with slips, trips and falls, office machinery and equipment, lifts and escalators, the use of access equipment, such as step ladders, poor housekeeping and hand tools. Many accidents arise as a result of inadequate lighting, particularly on staircases and in storage areas.

Health risks include tenosynovitis, visual fatigue and postural fatigue associated with the use of keyboards and DISPLAY SCREEN EQUIPMENT (DSE).

Fire

Fire hazards may be the result of defective wiring and sockets, overloading of electrical circuits and the use of free-standing heating appliances. The majority of office machinery is now electrically operated and many offices are not equipped with sufficient power outlets to meet this demand. This results in the use of multi-point adaptors, extension leads and the wiring of more than one appliance into a 13 amp plug. All these forms of electrical abuse and misuse greatly increase the risk of fire.

Many materials used in offices, such as spirit-based cleaning fluids, floor polishes and packing materials, are highly flammable and careless storage can be a contributory factor in fires and their spread. Smoking also represents a fire hazard and a high proportion of office fires have been caused by the careless disposal of cigarette ends and matches.

Fire prevention measures in the office should incorporate:

1. a total ban on the use of free-standing heating appliances;
2. examination of electrical circuits by a competent engineer every ten years;
3. storage of flammable substances in lockable metal cabinets;
4. control over the storage of waste paper and packing materials;
5. quarterly test of the fire alarm;
6. an annual fire drill;
7. annual servicing of the appliances;
8. the training of key personnel in the use of fire appliances;
9. the training and appointment of competent persons as fire wardens.

Slips, trips and falls

These forms of accident are common in offices. Typical causes include:

1. people engaging in unsafe activities – walking while reading, tripping over the bottom drawer of a filing cabinet which has been left open, rushing, opening swing doors violently (clear view panels should be fitted), standing on a swivel chair to reach stored items;
2. structural items – wet floors, spillages on floors and staircases, defective or slippery floor finishes, badly designed handrails to staircases;
3. unsuitable footwear for office use.

Machinery

The Provision and Use of Work Equipment Regulations 1998 (PUWER) require that any form of work equipment shall be suitable for the purpose for which it is used, and be maintained in an efficient state, in efficient working order and in good repair. Where the use of such equipment involves a specific risk (e.g. amputation), the use is restricted to persons specifically given the task of using it. Repairs, modifications, maintenance or servicing must be restricted to designated persons, who have been trained for the purpose.

Lifts

Lifts must be inspected regularly and well maintained, with care being taken to ensure that lift cars level off correctly at their various landings in order to reduce the risk of people tripping. Lift cars must be marked with the maximum safe working load and also state the maximum number of passengers who may be carried at one time. Lift cars should incorporate some form of alarm in the event of a breakdown between floors.

Access equipment

All forms of access equipment should be inspected on a regular basis, and staff who use ladders should be instructed in their safe use. Ladders should be fitted with anti-slip feet, and no work should be undertaken from the upper steps of a stepladder unless it is fitted with a handrail or is of the platform type.

Hand tools

Many minor injuries result from the misuse of items such as scissors, razor blades and knives in offices. Safety knives only should be used, and certainly not razor blades of any type.

Manual handling

Employees should be trained in correct lifting and handling techniques. In certain cases trolleys and other manual handling aids should be provided when moving heavy items such as typewriters.

Hazardous substances

Certain substances used in offices may be toxic, corrosive, irritant, flammable or otherwise harmful. Depending on the type of substance and its mode of use, it may be necessary to undertake health risk assessment under the Control of Substances Hazardous to Health Regulations 1999 (COSHHR). Staff should be provided with information on the correct use of HAZARDOUS SUBSTANCES, trained in safe working procedures and regularly supervised.

Competent persons

Introduction

Modern health and safety legislation places considerable emphasis on an employer appointing 'competent persons' to undertake a range of tasks where there may be a high degree of risk and/or where special expertise may be required.

The expression 'competent person' occurs frequently in construction safety law. For example, under the Construction (Health, Safety and Welfare) Regulations 1996, certain inspections, examinations, operations and supervisory duties must be undertaken by competent persons.

However, the term is not generally defined in law except in the Electricity at Work Regulations 1989 and the Pressure Systems and Transportable Gas Containers Regulations 1989. Therefore the onus is on the employer to decide whether persons are competent to undertake these duties. An employer might do this by reference to the person's training, qualifications, skills and experience. Alternatively, the competent person function may be undertaken by an external specialists on behalf of an employer. Insurance companies commonly provide a competent person service, for instance, for the examination and testing of pressure systems and lifting appliances.

Duties and functions of competent persons

Management of Health and Safety at Work Regulations 1999

A competent person or persons must be appointed:

1. To assist the employer in undertaking the measures he needs to take to comply with the requirements and prohibitions imposed upon him by or under the relevant statutory provisions. In this case, a person shall be regarded as competent where he has sufficient training and experience or knowledge and other qualities to enable him properly to assist the employer in undertaking the above measures.
2. To implement the procedures for serious and imminent danger and for

danger areas in so far as they relate to the evacuation from premises of persons at work in an employer's undertaking.

Where there is a competent person in the employer's employment, that person shall be appointed for the purposes of (1) above in preference to a competent person not in his employment.

Lifting Operations and Lifting Equipment Regulations (LOLER) 1998

The duties of competent persons under these regulations with respect to the 'thorough examination' and 'inspection' of lifting equipment, together with the making of reports, are extensive.

The regulations require employers to ensure the following thorough examinations and inspections are undertaken by competent persons.

1. In the case of lifting equipment for lifting people, and where there are no suitable devices to prevent the risk of a carrier falling, inspection of the rope or chain to that carrier every working day.
2. The planning of lifting operations involving lifting equipment.
3. Thorough examination for any defect in lifting equipment before being put into service for the first time unless either:

    (a) the lifting equipment has not been used before; and
    (b) in the case of lifting equipment for which an EC declaration of conformity could or (in the case of a declaration under the Lifts Regulations 1997) should have been drawn up, the employer has received such declaration made not more than twelve months before the lifting equipment is put into service; or if obtained from the undertaking of another person, it is accompanied by the appropriate physical evidence i.e. that the last thorough examination required to be carried out under Regulation 9 has been carried out.

4. Where the safety of lifting equipment depends upon the installation conditions, thorough examination:

    (a) after installation and before being put into service for the first time; and
    (b) after assembly and before being put into service at a new site or in a new location.

5. Where lifting equipment is exposed to conditions causing deterioration which is liable to result in dangerous situations:

    (a) thorough examination:
        (i) in the case of lifting equipment for lifting persons or an accessory for lifting, at least every six months;

(ii) in the case of other lifting equipment, at least every twelve months; or

(iii) in either case, in accordance with an examination scheme; and

(iv) each time that exceptional circumstances which are liable to jeopardise the safety of the lifting equipment have occurred; and

(b) if appropriate for the purpose, inspection by a competent person at suitable intervals between thorough examinations, to ensure that health and safety conditions are maintained and that any deterioration can be detected and remedied in good time.

6. Following a thorough examination for an employer of lifting equipment under 5 above, a competent person must:

(a) notify the employer forthwith of any defect in the lifting equipment which in his opinion is or could become a danger to persons;

(b) as soon as is practicable make a report of the thorough examination in writing authenticated by him or on his behalf by signature or equally secure means and containing the information specified in Schedule 1 to:

(i) the employer; and

(ii) any person from whom the lifting equipment has been hired or leased;

(c) where there is in his opinion a defect in the lifting equipment involving an existing or imminent risk of serious personal injury send a copy of the report as soon as is practicable to the relevant enforcing authority.

7. A person making an inspection for an employer must:

(a) notify the employer forthwith of any defect in the lifting equipment which in his opinion is or could become a danger to persons;

(b) as soon as is practicable make a record of the inspection in writing.

Provision and Use of Work Equipment Regulations (PUWER) 1998

These regulations make reference to both 'inspection' and 'thorough inspection' of work equipment. In the case of the inspection of work equipment, this means:

1. such visual or more rigorous inspection by a competent person as is appropriate for the purpose described in that paragraph; and

2. where it is appropriate to carry out testing for the purpose, includes testing the nature and extent of which are appropriate for the purpose.

In the case of a thorough examination of power presses, guards and protection devices, 'thorough inspection' means:

1. a thorough examination by a competent person; and
2. includes testing the nature and extent of which are appropriate for the purpose described in the paragraph.

Noise at Work Regulations 1989

A competent person must make a noise assessment which is adequate for the purpose of:

1. identifying employees' noise exposure; and
2. providing the employer with appropriate information as to enable him to facilitate compliance with his duties.

Pressure Systems and Transportable Gas Containers Regulations 1989

Owners and users of pressure systems must have a Written Scheme of Examination drawn up by a competent person for the examination of the system at specified intervals. Competence is based on the type of work undertaken, i.e. minor, intermediate or major systems (as defined).

The competent person:

1. advises user on the scope of the Written Scheme of Examination;
2. draws up or certifies Schemes of Examination;
3. undertakes examinations under the Scheme.

Electricity at Work Regulations 1989

These regulations stipulate that no person must carry out a work activity where technical knowledge or experience is necessary to prevent danger or injury, unless he has such knowledge or is under the appropriate degree of supervision. (Whilst the term does not appear, competence is implied.)

Construction (Design and Management) Regulations 1994

Competence must be taken into account by:

1. a client when appointing a planning supervisor;
2. any person when arranging for a designer to prepare a design;
3. any person when arranging for a contractor to carry out or manage construction work.

Construction (Health, Safety and Welfare) Regulations 1996 (CHSWR)

Competent persons must be appointed for:

Table 1 CHSWR Schedule 7: Places of work requiring inspection

Place of work	Time of inspection
1. Any working platform of part thereof or any personal suspension equipment	(i) Before being put into use for the first time; and
	(ii) after any substantial addition, dismantling or other alteration; and
	(iii) after any event likely to have affected its strength and stability; and
	(iv) at regular intervals not exceeding seven days since the last inspection
2. Any excavation which is supported	(i) Before any person carries out work at the start of every shift; and
	(ii) after any event likely to have affected the strength or stability of the excavation or any part thereof; and
	(iii) after any accidental fall of rock or earth or other material
3. Cofferdams and caissons	(i) Before any person starts every shift; and
	(ii) after any event likely to have affected the strength or stability of the cofferdam or caisson or any part thereof

1. Supervision of:
    (a) the installation or erection of any scaffold and any substantial addition or alteration to a scaffold;
    (b) the installation or erection of any personal suspension equipment or any means of arresting falls;
    (c) erection or dismantling of any buttress, temporary support or temporary structure used to support a permanent structure;
    (d) demolition or dismantling of any structure, or any part of any structure, being demolition or dismantling which gives rise to a risk of danger to any person;
    (e) installation, alteration or dismantling of any support for an excavation;

    (f) construction, installation, alteration or dismantling of a cofferdam or

    (g) caisson; and

    (h) the safe transport of any person conveyed by water to or from any place of work.

2. Inspection of places of work as specified in Schedule 7 to the Regulations (see Table 1, p. 17).

Contractors

Introduction

A contractor is generally defined as a person who provides a contract of service or a contract for service. Contractors provide a range of services to organisations, such as maintenance of plant and equipment, catering, cleaning, the provision of goods and the extension and modification of premises, Contractors undertaking construction work are, in most cases, regulated by the Construction (Design and Management) Regulations (CDMR) 1994 and the Construction (Health, Safety and Welfare) Regulations 1996. Where construction work involves lifting operations and lifting equipment, the Lifting Operations and Lifting Equipment Regulations 1998 (LOLER) also apply.

Traditionally, the construction industry has not had a good record with regard to accidents and this fact has been recognised in the need for the above legislation. Both clients and contractors need, therefore, to have safety management systems and procedures well established before work commences.

Construction safety

Principal hazards

The construction industry has always ranked as one of the more dangerous industries. Accidents may be associated with any of the following:

1. ladders;
2. falls from working platforms;
3. falls of materials;
4. falls from pitched roofs and through fragile roofs;
5. falls through openings in flat roofs and floors;
6. collapses of excavations;
7. transport;
8. machinery and powered hand tools;
9. poor housekeeping;
10. fire;
11. failure to provide or wear personal protective equipment.

Construction (Design and Management) Regulations 1994 (CDMR)

The CDMR specify the relationships that must exist between a client, principal contractor and other contractors from a health and safety viewpoint. Under these Regulations certain people have both general and specific duties.

The client (the person for whom the project is carried out), must:

1. appoint a planning supervisor and a principal contractor for each project;
2. ensure that the planning supervisor has been given relevant information about the state or condition of specified premises; and
3. ensure that a health and safety file is available for the inspection of specified persons.

The planning supervisor must ensure that specified particulars of a notifiable project are sent to the Health and Safety Executive (HSE). Planning supervisors have specific duties in respect of:

1. the design of any structure comprised in the project;
2. cooperation between designers;
3. giving adequate advice to specified persons;
4. the preparation, review and necessary amendment of a health and safety file; and
5. the delivery of the health and safety file to the client.

The principal contractor has a number of duties in respect of:

1. cooperation between contractors;
2. compliance with the health and safety plan;
3. the exclusion of unauthorised persons;
4. the display of notices;
5. the provision of information to the planning supervisor;
6. the provision of certain health and safety information to contractors and the provision of specified information and training to the employees of those contractors;
7. ensuring that the views and advice of persons at work on the project or their representatives concerning matters relating to their health and safety are received, discussed and coordinated.

The principal contractor is empowered, for certain purposes, to give directions to contractors and to include rules in the health and safety plan.

The designer:

1. is prohibited from preparing a design unless the client for the project is aware of his or her duties under the Regulations and of the require-

ments of any practical guidance issued by the Health and Safety Commission (HSC); and

2. must ensure that the design he or she prepares, and which is to be used for the purposes of construction work or cleaning work, takes into account among design considerations certain specified matters.

The contractor(s) (other than the principal contractor) must cooperate with the principal contractor in order to enable that contractor to comply with the duties outlined above.

A person who appoints a planning supervisor, or who arranges for a designer to prepare a design, or a contractor to carry out or manage construction work, is prohibited from doing so unless reasonably satisfied:

1. as to the competence of those so appointed or arranged; and
2. as to the adequacy of the resource so allocated or to be allocated for the purposes of performing their respective functions by those so appointed or arranged.

Both the planning supervisor and principal contractor must comply with the requirements relating to the health and safety plan. The construction phase cannot commence unless a health and safety plan has been prepared for the project.

Competent persons

No person shall be appointed as agent by a client unless the client is reasonably satisfied as to that person's competence to perform the duties imposed on the client under the Regulations. Similarly, planning supervisors, designers and contractors must be competent to comply with any requirements and conduct the undertaking without contravening any prohibitions imposed by or under health and safety law.

Health and safety files

The following data must be incorporated in a health and safety file:

1. information included with the design which will enable the planning supervisor and designers to comply with legal requirements; and
2. any other information relating to the project which it is reasonably foreseeable will be necessary to ensure the health and safety of all persons involved in the project.

Health and safety plans

The planning supervisor shall ensure that a health and safety plan for the project has been prepared in sufficient time for it to be given to a contractor before arrangements are made to carry out or manage the construction work.

Under Regulation 15, the following information must be incorporated in the health and safety plan:

1. a general description of the construction work to be undertaken in the project;
2. details of the time in which it is intended that the project, and any intermediate stages, will be completed;
3. details of the risks to the health or safety of any person carrying out the construction work so far as such risks are known to the planning supervisor or are reasonably foreseeable;
4. any other information concerning the competence of the planning supervisor and the availability of resources to enable him or her to undertake specified duties;
5. information held by the planning supervisor and needed by the principal contractor to enable that contractor to comply with the specified duties; and
6. information held by the planning supervisor and which any contractor should know in order to comply with statutory provisions in respect of welfare.

The principal contractor must then take appropriate measures to ensure that the health and safety plan incorporates the necessary features to ensure the health and safety of everyone involved in the project.

Selecting and managing contractors

The HSE publication *A Guide to Managing Health and Safety in Construction* provides useful information for clients on the principal contractor's key tasks during the construction phase of a project. The principal contractor should:

1. develop and implement the health and safety plan;
2. be reasonably satisfied that when arranging for a contractor to carry out construction work, they are competent and have made adequate provision for health and safety;
3. obtain and check safety method statements from contractors;
4. ensure the coordination and cooperation of contractors (particularly under the Management of Health and Safety at Work Regulations 1999 and the Provision and Use of Work Equipment Regulations 1998);
5. ensure training for health and safety is carried out;
6. have appropriate communication arrangements between contractors on site for health and safety;
7. make arrangements for discussing health and safety matters with people on site;

8. allow only authorised people on site;
9. display notification details;
10. monitor health and safety performance;
11. pass information to the planning supervisor for the health and safety file.

When selecting a principal contractor the above tasks must be taken into consideration, including the contractor's management systems for ensuring the tasks are undertaken satisfactorily.

Construction (Health, Safety and Welfare) Regulations 1996

These regulations impose absolute requirements with respect to the health, safety and welfare of persons at work carrying out 'construction work' as defined and of others who may be affected by that work.

Subject to specific exceptions, the regulations impose requirements on duty holders, i.e. employers, the self-employed and others who control the way in which construction work is carried out. Employees have duties in respect of their own actions. Every person at work has duties as regards cooperation with others and the reporting of danger.

The principal duties of employers, the self-employed and controllers

Safe places of work

There is a general duty to ensure a safe place of work and means of access to and from that place. Specific provisions include the following:

Precautions against falls

1. prevention of falls from heights by physical precautions or, where this is not possible, provision equipment that will arrest falls;
2. provision and maintenance of physical precautions to prevent falls through fragile materials;
3. erection of scaffolding, access equipment, harnesses and nets under the supervision of a competent person;
4. specific criteria for using ladders.

Falling objects

1. where necessary to protect people at work and others, taking steps to prevent materials or objects from falling;
2. where it is not reasonably practicable to prevent falling materials, taking precautions to prevent people from being struck, e.g. covered walkways;

3. prohibition of throwing any materials or objects down from a height if they could strike someone;
4. storage of materials and equipment safely.

Work on structures

1   prevention of accidental collapse of new or existing structures or those under construction;
2. ensuring any dismantling or demolition of any structure is planned and carried out in a safe manner under the supervision of a competent person;
3. only firing explosive charges after steps have been taken to ensure that no one is exposed to risk or injury from the explosion.

Excavations, cofferdams and caissons

1. prevention of the collapse of ground both in and above excavations;
2. identification and prevention of risk from underground cables and other services;
3. ensuring cofferdams and caissons are properly designed, constructed and maintained.

Prevention or avoidance of drowning

1. taking steps to prevent people falling into water or other liquid so far as is reasonably practicable;
2. ensuring that personal protective and rescue equipment is immediately available for use and maintained, in the event of a fall;
3. ensuring sure transport by water is under the control of a competent person.

Traffic routes, vehicles, doors and gates

1. ensuring construction sites are organised so that pedestrians and vehicles can both move safely and without risks to health;
2. ensuring routes are suitable and sufficient for the people or vehicles using them;
3. prevention or control of the unintended movement of any vehicle;
4. ensuring arrangements for giving a warning of any possible dangerous movement, e.g. reversing vehicles;
5. ensuring safe operation of vehicles including prohibition of riding or remaining in unsafe positions;
6. ensuring doors and gates which could prevent danger, e.g. trapping risk of powered doors and gates, are provided with suitable safeguards.

Prevention and control of emergencies

1. prevention of risk from fire, explosion, flooding and asphyxiation;
2. provision of emergency routes and exits;
3. provision of arrangements for dealing with emergencies, including procedures for evacuating the site;
4. where necessary, provision of fire-fighting equipment, fire detectors and alarm systems.

Welfare facilities

1. provision of sanitary and washing facilities and an adequate supply of drinking water;
2. provision of rest facilities, facilities to change and store clothing.

Site-wide issues

1. ensuring sufficient fresh or purified air is available at every workplace, and that associated plant is capable of giving visible or audible warning of failure;
2. ensuring a reasonable working temperature is maintained at indoor workplaces during working hours;
3. provision of facilities for protection against adverse weather conditions;
4. ensuring suitable and sufficient emergency lighting is available;
5. ensuring suitable and sufficient lighting is available, including the provision of secondary lighting where there would be a risk to health or safety if the primary or artificial lighting failed;
6. maintaining construction sites in good order and in a reasonable state of cleanliness;
7. ensuring the perimeter of a construction site to which people, other than those working on the site could gain access, is marked by suitable signs so that its extent can be easily identified;
8. ensuring all plant and equipment used for construction work is safe, of sound construction and used and maintained so that it remains safe and without risks to health.

Training, inspection and reports

1. ensuring construction activities where training, technical knowledge or experience is necessary to reduce risks of injury are only carried out by people who meet these requirements or, if not, are supervised by those with appropriate training, knowledge or experience;
2. before work at height, on excavations, cofferdams or caissons begins, ensuring the place of work is inspected (and at subsequent specified

periods), by a competent person, who must be satisfied that the work can be done safely;

3. following inspection, ensuring written reports are made by the competent person.

See also COMPETENT PERSONS.

Contractors' Regulations

Many organisations have formal Contractors' Regulations or operating procedures in order to comply with the duties of employers towards non-employees under section 3 of the Health and Safety at Work etc. Act 1974 (HSWA), and the provisions of the Management of Health and Safety at Work Regulations 1999 with regard to shared workplaces. These Regulations are issued to a contractor undertaking any work on the organisation's premises or land. The may form part of the 'rules for the safe conduct of project work' under the Construction (Design and Management) Regulations (CDMR) issued by a client to a prospective contractor at the tendering stage.

It is a common condition of the Terms of Contract that contractors:

1. employ on site only people who are skilled, experienced and careful in the performance of their trades, callings and duties;
2. comply with general and specific requirements of the organisation's Contractors' Regulations; and
3. are not relieved of any of their obligations under statute and common law.

Confirmation of receipt of the Regulations should be confirmed in writing by all contractors.

Small-scale construction activities

The majority of construction operations tend to be small in scale and would not come within the scope of the CDM Regulations however. This could include, for instance, work carried out inside offices and shops without interrupting the normal activities in the premises or work undertaken on domestic premises, such as repairs to a roof or the installation of central heating. However, in such instances, the Construction (Health, Safety and Welfare) Regulations do apply where 'construction work', which is broadly defined in these regulations, is undertaken.

On this basis, employers, self-employed persons and occupiers of premises should ensure when selecting a contractor that, firstly, he is aware of the above requirements and, secondly, works safely to ensure compliance with same. Unsafe working practices, such as a failure to provide safe access to a roof, or to work safely when cleaning windows, should be drawn to the attention of the contractor immediately.

Display screen equipment

Introduction

Display screen equipment or visual display units have given some cause for concern since their introduction in the 1980s. A number of health risks were alleged to be associated with the use of this equipment to the extent that the European Union saw fit to produce a Directive on same (No. 90/270/EEC) on 29 May 1990. This Directive on 'minimum health and safety requirements for work with display screen equipment' was implemented in the UK as the Health and Safety (Display Screen Equipment) Regulations 1992.

Health and Safety (Display Screen Equipment) Regulations 1992

These Regulations came into operation on 1 January 1993 and should be read in conjunction with the Management of Health and Safety at Work Regulations 1999 (MHSWR). Under the Regulations, employers have a duty to ensure that workstations meet the requirements laid down in the Schedule. It is important when considering the implementation of these Regulations to appreciate the significance of four definitions shown in Regulation 1:

1. *Display screen equipment* (DSE) means an alphanumeric or graphic display screen, regardless of the display process involved.
2. *Operator* means a self-employed person who habitually uses display screen equipment as a significant part of his or her normal work.
3. *User* means an employee who habitually uses display screen equipment as a significant part of his or her normal work.
4. *Workstation* means an assembly comprising:
   (a) DSE;
   (b) any accessories to the DSE;
   (c) any disk drive, modem, printer, document holder, work chair, work desk, work surface or other item peripheral to the DSE; and
   (d) the immediate environment around the DSE.

The terms 'habitual' and 'significant' in the definition of both 'user' and 'operator' are important because many of those who use DSE as a feature of their work activities may not be users as defined. Employers must decide which of their employees are 'users' by referring to the Guidance which accompanies the Regulations.

The Regulations do *not* apply to or in relation to:

1. drivers' cabs or control cabs;
2. DSE on board a means of transport;
3. DSE mainly intended for public operation;
4. portable systems not in prolonged use;
5. calculators, cash registers or any equipment having a small data or measurement display required for direct use of the equipment; or
6. window typewriters.

Regulation 2 – Analysis of workstations

Regulation 2 is the principal requirement. Employers shall perform a suitable and sufficient analysis of those workstations which:

1. are used for the purposes of the undertaking by users (regardless of who has provided them); and
2. have been provided by and are used for the purposes of the undertaking by operators;

for the purpose of assessing the health and safety risks to which those persons are exposed in consequence of that use.

Regulation 4 – Daily work routines

This regulation requires that every employer shall ensure that users' daily work routine is periodically interrupted by breaks or changes of activity.

Regulation 5 – Eye and eyesight tests

Employers are required to make provision on request for eye and eyesight tests for existing users and people who become users, such tests to be undertaken by a registered ophthalmic optician or a registered medical practitioner with suitable qualifications.

Regulation 6 – Training

Employers shall ensure that existing and new users of DSE receive adequate health and safety training.

Regulation 7 – Provision of information

Regulation 7 states that every employer shall ensure that operators and users are provided with adequate information about all aspects of health and safety relating to their workstations.

DSE risk analysis

Risk analysis involves a consideration of the requirements laid down in the Schedule to the Regulations relating to the equipment, the environment and the interface between the computer and operator/user.

Display screen equipment – the risks

The three principal risks to health associated with the use of DSE are: work-related upper limb disorders; visual fatigue; and postural fatigue.

Work-related upper limb disorders

Work-related upper limb disorders caused by repetitive strain injuries (RSI) were first defined in the medical literature by Bernardo Ramazzini in the early eighteenth century. The International Labour Organisation recognised RSI as an occupational disease in 1960 as a condition caused by forceful, frequent, twisting and repetitive movements.

RSI covers some well-known conditions such as tennis elbow, flexor tenosynovitis and carpal tunnel syndrome. It is usually caused or aggravated by work, and is associated with repetitive and over-forceful movement, excessive workloads, inadequate rest periods and sustained or constrained postures, resulting in pain or soreness due to the inflammatory conditions of muscles and the synovial lining of the tendon sheath. Treatment is largely effective, if the condition is treated in its early stages. Tenosynovitis has been a prescribed industrial disease since 1975, and the Health and Safety Executive (HSE) have proposed changing the name of the condition to 'work-related upper limb disorder' on the grounds that the disorder does not always result from repetition or strain, and is not always a visible injury.

Injury can be prevented by:

1. improved design of working areas, e.g. position of keyboard and visual display unit (VDU) screens, heights of workbenches and chairs;
2. adjustments of workloads and rest periods;
3. provision of special tools;
4. health surveillance aimed at detecting early stages of the disorder; and
5. better training and supervision.

If untreated, RSI can be seriously disabling.

Operational stress

This can take the form of both visual fatigue and postural fatigue.

Visual fatigue

Visual fatigue (eye strain) is associated with glare from the display screen and the need continually to focus and refocus from screen to copy material and back again. The degree of individual fatigue will vary. Vision screening of staff on a regular basis and as part of a pre-employment health screen is recommended.

Postural fatigue

Postural fatigue, an outcome of operational stress, can take many forms. It can include backache, neck and shoulder pains associated with poor chair and workstation design and positioning in relation to controls and displays, insufficient leg room and the need to adjust body position.

Other causes of operational stress

Operational stress can also be created by noise from the unit and ancillary equipment, excessive heat and inadequate ventilation.

Introduction

Every year people die as a result of unsound working practices involving electricity. Others may suffer electric shock and deep-seated burns through direct contact with electrical energy. The Electricity at Work Regulations 1989 and the accompanying HSE Memorandum of Guidance, together with the Institution of Electrical Engineers' Regulations for Electical Installations (the 'Wiring Regulations'), provide excellent guidance on electrical safety issues and should always be followed.

Hazards associated with the use of electricity can broadly be divided into two categories: the risk of injuries to people and the risk of fire and/or explosion.

Injury to people

Injury is associated with shock, burns, injuries from explosions, micro-waves, accumulators and batteries, and eye injuries.

Electric shock

This is the effect produced on the body and, in particular, the nervous system by an electric current passing through it. The effect varies according to the strength of the current which, in turn, varies with the voltage and the electrical resistance of the body. The resistance of the body will vary according to the points of entry and exit of the current and other factors, such as body weight and/or the presence of moisture (see Table 2).

Table 2 Typical responses to current and voltage

Voltage	Response	Current
15 volts	Threshold of feeling	0.002–0.005 amps
205 volts	Threshold of pain	0.005–0.01 amps
30 volts	Muscular spasm (non-release)	0.015 amps
70 volts	Minimum for death	0.1 amps
120 volts	Maximum for 'safety'	0.002 amps
20,040 volts	Most serious/fatal accidents	0.2 amps

First aid

First aid for a victim of electric shock must be cardiac massage plus mouth-to-mouth resuscitation until normal breathing and the heart action return. A victim who is 'locked on' to a live appliance must not be approached until the appliance is electrically dead.

Burns

A current passing through a conductor produces heat. Burns can be caused by contact with hot conductors or by the passage of a current through the body at the point of entry and exit. Electric arcing from short circuits may also cause burns.

Explosion

Electrical shortcircuit or sparking from the electrical contacts in switches or other equipment is a common cause of explosions and consequent injury or death.

Microwave apparatus

Microwaves can damage the soft tissues of the body.

Accumulators and batteries

Hydrogen gas may be produced as a by-product of battery charging and can cause explosive atmospheres with the risk of burns.

Eye injuries

These can arise from exposure to ultraviolet rays from accidental arcing as in shortcircuits or arcing in a process, such as welding.

Fire

Electricity is a common source of ignition for major FIRES. Some insulating materials and materials used for electrical connections are flammable and can give rise to small fires in switchgear, distribution boxes or sub-stations. Sources of electrical ignition include: sparks, arcs, shortcircuits, and old and defective/damaged wiring.

Principles of electrical safety

There are two basic preventive measures against electric shock:

1. protection against direct contact, e.g. insulation of equipment, and

2. protection against indirect contact, e.g. by providing effective earthing.

Earthing

When an earth fault exists, such as when a live part touches an enclosed conductive part (e.g. metalwork), it is vital to ensure that the electrical supply is automatically disconnected. This can be brought about by the use of overcurrent devices (i.e. correctly rated fuses or circuit-breakers), or by correctly rated and placed residual current devices. The maintenance of earth continuity is vital.

Reduced voltage

Reduced voltage systems are another form of protection against electric shock, the most commonly used being the 100 volt centre point earthed system. In this system the secondary winding of the transformer providing the 110 volt supply is centre tapped to earth, thereby ensuring that at no part of the 110 volt circuit can the voltage to earth exceed 55 volts.

Safe systems of work

Where work is to be undertaken on electrical apparatus or a part of a circuit, a formally operated safe system of work should be followed. This normally takes the form of a permit to work system.

Fire and explosion prevention

The principles of insulation, isolation, circuit protection and minimising supply and equipment voltages apply both to the prevention of fire and explosion and to the prevention of injury.

Further protection of potentially flammable atmospheres using flameproof or sparkproof equipment and/or the siting of switchgear, etc., away from risk areas must also be considered.

Automatic inerting of switchrooms and sub-stations or flooding with extinguishant gas is often used as a precaution against potential fire damage where the equipment is valuable, e.g. computer installations.

Portable electrical equipment

The hazards described above for all electrical equipment and circuits apply but are made worse by the portable nature of the equipment and tools.

Precautions

Specific precautions relating to portable electrical equipment and appliances include:

1. the use of low voltage circuits and equipment;
2. the use of all-insulated appliances, i.e. conductors are insulated, plus a protective case of tough insulating material;
3. the use of double-insulated appliances, i.e. conductors insulated together with a general insulation beneath the metal cladding or the case;
4. the use of current-operated circuit-breaker adaptation to power outlets;
5. regular checks on earth continuity, the condition of flexible cables and cable connections, and circuit protection in circuits used for portable equipment.

Flameproof equipment

Potentially flammable hazardous areas are classified according to a graded probability of an explosive gas or vapour concentration occurring.

The principle of flameproofing is to ensure that the apparatus so described is constructed to withstand any explosion within the apparatus, arising from ignition of flammable gas which may enter through the casing or other enclosure. All flanges and other joints of the casing or enclosure of the apparatus are well designed and constructed so as to prevent any internal ignition of gas from moving out of the enclosure and igniting a surrounding flammable atmosphere.

Electrical testing

Electrical testing is necessary to ensure that the design, construction and performance specifications of the items being tested are maintained at an adequate standard for the anticipated continued use. Electrical testing also enables faults to be detected so that remedial measures can be taken before the fault develops and damage or personal injury arises.

Types of testing

1. *Routine testing of production lines*

Equipment such as electric motors and various types of industrial, commercial and domestic apparatus requires individual or batch testing. Procedures include resistance and insulation tests for correct connection and operation. Those undertaking the tests should be competent to do so. The layout of the work area should not expose anyone to live and other dangerous parts.

2. *Testing of electrical installations*

A prerequisite to such testing is visual inspection to ensure that all circuits and equipment comply with an accepted standard and are properly installed, and that circuit protection and earthing arrangements appear in good order.

Ordinary test lamps and leads with exposed test prods or even bare ends have caused numerous flashovers, and the dangerous practice of using metal lampholders is, unfortunately, still encountered. Properly designed, protected and approved test equipment, employing current limiting resistors, well-shrouded test prods and properly insulated handles are available and should always be used.

It is a requirement of the Institute of Electrical Engineers (IEE) Wiring Regulations that on final circuits the circuit protective device, e.g. fuse or miniature circuit breaker, will, in the event of a fault to earth, operate within 0.4 seconds for socket outlets in bathrooms and outdoor circuits, and within 0.5 seconds for circuits supplying fixed equipment.

Training of personnel

A key to safe working on electrical installations and apparatus is that all those engaged on such work shall have been adequately trained. Both off-the-job and on-the-job training must be properly supervised, and at each stage the trainee must be made aware of the extent and limitations of the job in hand, the hazards that may be present and the precautions that have to be taken to ensure safe working.

Electrical safety in offices

General electrical safety requirements

1. All accessible parts of electrically operated equipment should be efficiently earthed.
2. All live terminals should be efficiently screened. In particular, operator access to parts of equipment should not allow access to live electrical parts at the same time.
3. Interlock switches provided for guards should prohibit inadvertent operation. The standard of maintenance and frequency of testing are important.
4. All flexible cords, plugs, sockets and couplers should be of good quality and standard. Flexible cables should be of adequate size, construction and protection, with approved connections and colour coding.
5. Mains input switches should be suitably placed on equipment with the ON and OFF positions identified and accessible.

6. An effective overcurrent protective device should be provided in each phase of the circuit and so arranged as to disconnect the electricity supply to the equipment in the event of overload or shortcircuit.

7. All high-voltage terminals and live conductors should be securely screened and a suitable warning notice indicating the danger displayed in a prominent position.

8. Where fluids are used in any machine, they should be housed so that they do not come into contact with electrical conductors and components. In the case of flammable liquids, special attention should be given to the machine enclosure to prevent dangerous concentrations of vapour building up. All electrical conductors and components should be specifically housed or constructed so as to avoid a risk of fire or explosion.

9. Where heating elements are incorporated in any machine, they should be placed and installed so as to cause no deterioration of electrical equipment or overheating that could create hazards to individuals.

Electrical installations

1. The installation, repair and maintenance of all electrical installations and equipment should be undertaken by competent persons only.

2. Equipment should be regularly inspected and serviced and staff should be encouraged to report any defects. Defective equipment should be taken out of service immediately.

3. Before anyone attempts to repair, service or adjust any electrically operated machine or equipment, or to remove the cover of such equipment, it should be disconnected from the power supply.

4. All wiring should be sound and regularly maintained.

5. Circuits should not be overloaded, particularly by the use of a single-socket outlet for more than one item. All circuits should incorporate overcurrent protection in the form of properly rated and positioned circuit breakers or fuses.

6. Staff should be trained in safety procedures and treatment in the event of electric shock.

Electricity at Work Regulations 1989

These Regulations, which replace the 1908 and 1944 Regulations and extend to all premises and not just those defined as factories under the Factories Act 1961, are made under the Health and Safety at Work etc. Act 1974 (HSWA). They require precautions to be taken against the risk of death or personal injury from electricity in work activities.

The Regulations establish general principles and impose duties on persons ('duty holders') in respect of systems, electrical equipment and conductors and in respect of work activities on or near electrical equipment.

Further detailed advice is given in the supporting Memorandum of Guidance and other authoritative documents.

Duties in some of the Regulations are subject to the qualifying term 'reasonably practicable'. Where qualifying terms are absent, the requirement is said to be absolute and must be met regardless of cost or any other consideration.

Regulation 29 provides a defence for a duty holder who can establish that she or he took all reasonable steps and exercised all due diligence to avoid committing an offence under certain Regulations.

In summary, the Regulations cover the following areas:

Regulation 2 – Interpretation. This regulation incorporates a number of important definitions.

Regulation 3 – Persons on whom duties are imposed. Equal levels of duty are imposed on employers, the self-employed, the manager of a mine or quarry, and employees.

Regulation 4 – Systems, work activities and protective equipment. All systems shall at all times be of such construction as to prevent, so far as is reasonably practicable, danger.

Regulation 5 – Strength and capability of electrical equipment. This regulation places an absolute duty to ensure that the strength and capability of electrical equipment in use are not exceeded in such a way as to give rise to danger.

Regulation 6 – Adverse or hazardous environments. Full account must be taken of any reasonably foreseeable adverse or hazardous environmental conditions.

Regulation 7 – Insulation, protection and placing of conductors. All conductors in a system which may give rise to danger shall either: (a) be suitably covered with insulating material or (b) have precautions taken to prevent, so far as is reasonably practicable, danger.

Regulation 8 – Earthing or other suitable precautions. The main emphasis of this regulation is on the provision of earthing. However, it is also recognised that other techniques may be employed, e.g. double insulation, connection to a common voltage reference point on the system, separated or isolated systems, etc.

Regulation 9 – Integrity of referenced conductors. The object of this regulation is to prevent referenced circuit conductors, which should be at or about the same potential as the reference point, from reaching significantly different potentials thereby giving rise to possible danger.

Regulation 10 – Connections. All joints and connections in a system must be

37

mechanically and electrically suitable for use. This requirement applies whether the installation is permanent or temporary.

Regulation 11 – Means for protecting from excess of current. This regulation requires the provision of efficient means, suitably located, to protect every part of a system from excess of current as may be necessary to prevent danger.

Regulation 12 – Means for cutting off the supply and for isolation. 'Isolation' here means the disconnection and separation of the electrical equipment from every source of electrical energy in such a way that the disconnection and separation are secure. (The requirements relating to isolation and separation do not apply to electrical equipment that is itself a source of electrical energy.)

Regulation 13 – Precautions for work on equipment made dead. Adequate precautions must be taken to prevent electrical equipment, which has been made dead, from becoming electrically charged during work.

Regulation 14 – Work on or near live conductors. This regulation imposes an absolute duty not to carry out work on or so near any live conductor that danger may arise unless:

(a) it is unreasonable in all the circumstances for it to be dead;

(b) it is reasonable in all the circumstances for the person concerned to be at work on or near it while it is live; and

(c) suitable precautions (including where necessary the provision of suitable protective equipment) are taken to prevent injury.

A written policy statement may be needed which establishes the need for live working to be permitted.

Regulation 15 – Working space, access and lighting. This is a general requirement that adequate working space, adequate means of access and adequate lighting at all electrical equipment be provided.

Regulation 16 – Persons to be competent to prevent danger and injury. The need to identify 'competent persons' for certain classes of electrical work is made clear in this regulation. Employers must also match the level of competence to the degree of supervision necessary.

Regulation 29 – Defence. In any proceedings for an offence consisting of a contravention of Regulations 4(4), 5, 8, 9, 10, 11, 12, 13, 14, 15, 16 or 25, it shall be a defence for any person to prove that he or she took all reasonable precautions and exercised all due diligence to avoid the commission of that offence.

Environmental factors

Introduction

The working environment embraces a number of important aspects. Apart from factors such as temperature, lighting and ventilation in the workplace, it includes areas such as structural safety, cleanliness, welfare amenity provision and the organisation of traffic routes.

Under the Health and Safety at Work etc. Act 1974 (HSWA) an employer must provide and maintain a working environment that is, so far as reasonably practicable, safe, without risks to health and adequate as regards facilities and arrangements for the welfare of employees at work. These duties are significantly extended in the Workplace (Health, Safety and Welfare) Regulations 1992 (WHSWR) and in specific regulations, such as the Health and Safety (Display Screen Equipment) Regulations 1992.

General safety in the workplace

Regulations 9–19 of the WHSWR lay down general and specific criteria for ensuring safety in the workplace.

Regulation 9 – Cleanliness and waste materials

Every workplace and its furniture, furnishings and fittings shall be kept sufficiently clean.

The surfaces of the floor, wall and ceiling of all workplaces inside buildings shall be capable of being kept sufficiently cleaned.

So far as is reasonably practicable, waste materials shall not be allowed to accumulate, except in suitable receptacles.

Regulation 10 – Room dimensions and space

Every room where persons work shall have sufficient floor area, height and unoccupied space for the purposes of health, safety and welfare.

It shall be sufficient compliance with this regulation if any existing workplace was subject to the provisions of the Factories Act 1961 if the workplace does not contravene Part 1 of Schedule 1.

Regulation 11 – Workstations and seating

Every workstation shall be so arranged that it is suitable both for any person at work in the workplace who is likely to work at that workstation and for any work of the undertaking which is likely to be done there.

Every workstation outdoors shall be so arranged that:

(a) so far as is reasonably practicable, it provides protection from adverse weather;

(b) it enables any person at the workstation to leave it swiftly or, as appropriate, to be assisted in the event of emergency; and

(c) it ensures that any person at the workstation cannot slip or fall.

A suitable seat shall be provided for each person at work in the workplace whose work includes operations of a kind that the work (or a substantial part of it) can or must be done sitting.

Regulation 12 – Condition of floors and traffic routes

Every floor in a workplace and the surface of every traffic route in a workplace shall be of a construction that is suitable for the purpose for which it is used.

So far as is reasonably practicable, every floor in a workplace and the surface of every traffic route in a workplace shall be kept free from obstructions and from any article or substance which may cause a person to slip, trip or fall.

Suitable and sufficient handrails and, if appropriate, guards shall be provided on all traffic routes which are staircases except in circumstances in which a handrail cannot be provided without obstructing the traffic route.

Regulation 13 – Falls or falling objects

So far as is reasonably practicable, suitable and effective measures shall be taken to prevent:

(a) any person falling a distance likely to cause personal injury;

(b) any person being struck by a falling object likely to cause personal injury.

Any area where there is a risk to health or safety from any of the above events shall be clearly indicated where appropriate.

So far as is reasonably practicable, every tank, pit or structure where there is a risk of a person in the workplace falling into a dangerous substance in the tank pit or structure, shall be securely covered or fenced.

Every traffic route over, across or in an uncovered tank, pit or structure shall be securely fenced.

Regulation 14 – Windows and transparent or translucent doors, gates and walls

These must be:

(a) constructed of safety material or be protected against breakage of the material; and
(b) appropriately marked or incorporate features so as, in either case, to make it apparent.

Regulation 15 – Windows, skylights and ventilators

No window, skylight or ventilator which is capable of being opened shall be likely to be opened, closed or adjusted in a manner which exposes any person performing such operation to a risk to his health or safety.

No window, skylight or ventilator shall be in a position which is likely to expose any person in the workplace to a risk to his or her health or safety.

Regulation 16 – Ability to clean windows, etc., safely

All windows and skylights in a workplace shall be of a design or so constructed that they may be cleaned safely.

Regulation 17 – Organisation, etc., of traffic routes

Every workplace shall be organised in such a way that pedestrians and vehicles can circulate safely.

All traffic routes shall be suitably indicated where necessary for reasons of health or safety.

Regulation 18 – Doors and gates

Doors and gates shall be suitably constructed (including being fitted with any necessary safety devices).

Regulation 19 – Escalators and moving walkways

Escalators and moving walkways shall:

(a) function safely;
(b) be equipped with any necessary safety devices;
(c) be fitted with one or more emergency stop control which is easily identifiable and readily accessible.

The organisation of the working environment

The majority of the duties on employers under the WHSWR are of an absolute or strict nature, compared with the duties, for instance, under the HSWA, which are qualified by the term 'so far as is reasonably practicable'.

Location of workplaces

Due consideration should be given to the locality, the density of surrounding buildings, availability of vehicle parking areas, access for employees and transport, including employees' own vehicles, and for fire, ambulance and police vehicles. The need for a well-organised traffic control system, which does not expose pedestrians to risk or injury, must be considered.

Layout of workplaces

An efficient layout should make a material contribution to preventing or reducing overcrowding, minimising the physical and mental effort required to perform the operations, expediting the process in an orderly and sequential flow, and ensuring maximum safety and hygiene standards throughout. A well-planned layout should eliminate the problem of overcrowding.

Structural safety

Attention must be paid to the structural safety aspects of:

1. floors, corridors, passageways and traffic routes;
2. stairs, ladders and catwalks;
3. underground rooms; and
4. external areas and approach roads.

See also STRUCTURAL SAFETY.

Cleanliness and waste disposal

The establishment of formal cleaning schedules and their implementation, together with a well-run refuse disposal operation, is vital to ensure compliance with Regulation 9.

Environmental stressors

Environmental stress, associated with extremes of temperature, poor standards of lighting and ventilation, noise and vibration, is a contributory factor to accidents. Many forms of occupational ill-health are directly associated with a failure to provide a healthy working environment.

Introduction

Death and damage associated with fire is, perhaps, the greatest loss to organisations. Whilst many fires may arise through hot processes, defective electrical equipment and the burning of refuse, what is of considerable concern is the increasing number of fires associated with the criminal offence of arson. In many cases fires are started by children and young persons.

Very few people actually die as a result of direct contact with fire, however. Most deaths are associated with asphyxiation following the inhalation of smoke and other by-products of fire.

Any consideration of fire safety procedures must, therefore, take into account security arrangements directed at preventing access by intruders at times when premises are unoccupied.

The main causes of fire and fire spread

Various studies by the Fire Protection Association of a range of industrial fires have indicated the following as the principal sources of fire in production and storage areas:

Production areas

1. heat-producing plant and equipment;
2. frictional heat and sparks;
3. refrigeration plant;
4. electrical equipment, setting fire to:
   (a) materials being processed,
   (b) dust,
   (c) waste and packing materials.

Storage areas

1. intruders, including children;
2. cigarettes and matches;
3. refuse burning;

4. electrical equipment, setting fire to:
   (a) stored goods;
   (b) packing materials.

Fire procedures

The legal requirements relating to fire protection are covered by the Health and Safety at Work etc. Act 1974 (HSWA), Fire Precautions Act 1971 (FPA) and the Fire Precautions (Workplace) Regulations 1997.

In all cases, there is a general duty on both employers and occupiers of premises to ensure safety and provide information, instruction and training for staff. More specific duties include the training of employees (fire drills), displaying details of the action to be taken in the event of fire and record keeping. The nature, scope and frequency of fire drills and the training to be given to staff in the use of fire appliances are generally left to the discretion of the fire authority, which acts within the guidelines incorporated in the various Guides to the Fire Precautions Act 1971.

Fire certificates

A fire certificate shall be issued to a place of work in which:

1. more than twenty persons are employed to work at any one time; *or*
2. more than ten persons are employed elsewhere than on the ground floor; *or*
3. which are in the same building as other places of work and the sum total exceeds twenty or ten respectively; *or*
4. in the case of a factory if 'non-allowable' quantities of explosives or highly flammable materials are stored or used in or under the premises.

A fire certificate must specify clearly and in detail:

1. the use(s) of the premises;
2. the means of escape from the relevant building;
3. the means for ensuring the means of escape can be safely and effectively used;
4. means for raising the alarm;
5. means for fighting fire for the use of persons on the premises;
6. particulars of explosive and/or highly flammable materials used or stored.

It may also require maintenance of the means of escape, means of escape into other buildings, maintenance of other fire precautions, e.g. rising mains, fire detection equipment, details of training and records of such training, a limitation on numbers and on fixtures and fittings. Spiral staircases, escalators, lifts, lowering lines and throw-out ladders are not suitable means of escape.

General rules

The following general rules apply:

1. Fire doors must open outwards only and should not be locked. If they have to be locked for security purposes, they should be fitted with panic bolts or the keys kept in a designated key box close to the exit. A notice should indicate that the doors can be opened in case of fire.
2. A fire exit notice should be fitted to or above the fire exit doors.
3. Appropriate notices should be displayed along fire escape routes, which should be provided with emergency lighting.

Fire instructions

A fire instruction is a notice informing people of the action they should take on either: hearing the alarm or discovering a fire.

In addition to displaying fire instructions, people should receive training in evacuation procedures (i.e. fire drills), at least quarterly; and the alarm should be sounded weekly.

Key personnel should be trained in the correct use of fire appliances.

Fire alarm systems

BS 5839: Part 1: 1988 lays down guidelines to be followed for the installation of fire alarm systems. In larger buildings this may take the form of a mains-operated system with breakglass alarm call points, an automatic control unit and electrically operated bells or sirens. In small buildings it would be reasonable to accept a manually operated, dry battery or compressed air-operated gong, klaxon or bell. To avoid the possibility of the alarm point being close to the source of a fire, duplicate facilities are necessary.

Storage and use of flammable substances

The following factors need to be considered:

1. *Flammable liquids:* Separate storage; storage of smallest quantities in the work area; transport in closed containers; correct labelling; safe dispensing; fire appliances available during use and dispensing; adequate ventilation; no smoking or naked lights.
2. *Liquefied and compressed gases:* Store and transport in upright position; store in open, well-ventilated area out of direct sunlight; secure with

wall chains or racks; oxygen cylinders stored separately; no handling by the valves; no dropping or rolling of cylinders; turn off at bottle valve when not in use.

Management of fire procedures

It is essential that formal fire procedures are established and maintained. Fire prevention and protection is a key function of the competent persons appointed under the Management of Health and Safety at Work Regulations 1999 (MHSWR). In addition, the advice and guidance of the local fire authority and its officers (fire prevention officers) should always be sought, particularly where any work or alterations may require a change to the conditions of the fire certificate.

Fire Precautions (Workplaces) Regulations 1997

Under these regulations, in addition to providing fire-fighting equipment, detectors and alarms, an employer must take 'measures for fire-fighting' which are adapted to the nature of the activities undertaken and the size of his undertaking and of the workplace concerned, taking into account persons other than employees (e.g. members of the public, contractors) who may be present. This may include the training of key operators in fire-fighting techniques.

He must nominate employees to implement these measures and ensure that the number of such employees, their training and the equipment available to them are adequate taking into account the size of, and specific hazards involved in, the workplace concerned, and arrange any contacts with external emergency services.

First aid

Introduction

First aid means the skilled application of accepted principles of treatment on the occurrence of an accident or in the case of sudden illness, using facilities and materials available at the time.

The significant areas of first aid treatment are:

- restoration of breathing (resuscitation):
- control of bleeding; and
- prevention of collapse.

Health and Safety (First Aid) Regulations 1981

These Regulations apply to nearly all workplaces in the UK. Under the Regulations first aid means:

1. in cases where a person will need help from a medical practitioner or nurse, treatment for the purpose of preserving life and minimising the consequences of injury or illness until such help is obtained; and
2. treatment of minor injuries which would otherwise receive no treatment or which do not need treatment by a medical practitioner or nurse.

Duties of employers

Regulation 3 requires an employer to provide or ensure that there are provided such equipment and facilities as are adequate and appropriate in the circumstances for enabling first aid to be rendered to his or her employees if they are injured or become ill at work.

Approved Code of Practice (ACOP) 1990

The ACOP 1990 emphasises the duty of employers to consider a number of factors and determine for themselves what is adequate and appropriate in all the circumstances. Furthermore, where there are particular risks associated with the operation of an enterprise, the employer must ensure that first aiders receive training to deal with these specific risks.

The general guidance suggests that even in a typical office there ought to be a first aider for every fifty persons.

First aid boxes

There should be at least one first aid box; the contents are listed in the Health and Safety Executive (HSE) Guidance.

Equipment for first aid rooms

The following equipment and other items are recommended for first aid rooms:

- a sink with running hot and cold water;
- drinking water when not available on tap, together with disposable cups;
- soap and paper towels;
- smooth-topped work surfaces;
- a suitable store for first aid materials;
- suitable refuse containers lined with a disposable plastic bag;
- a couch with waterproof surface, together with frequently cleaned pillows and blankets;
- clean protective garments;
- a chair;
- an appropriate record (Form BI 510);
- a bowl.

Travelling first aid kits

The minimum contents for a travelling first aid kit are:

- one guidance card;
- six individually wrapped sterile adhesive dressings;
- one large sterile unmedicated dressing;
- two triangular bandages;
- two safety pins; and
- individually wrapped moist cleansing wipes.

Hazardous substances

Introduction

A wide range of hazardous substances is encountered in workplaces, including acids, alakalis, solvents, process chemicals and disinfectants. Exposure to these hazardous substances, apart from being responsible for many deaths at work, perhaps as a result of a gassing accident, can result in conditions such as dermatitis, various forms of poisoning and a range of secondary effects associated with the entry of these substances into the body. A comprehensive strategy for dealing with hazardous substances is, therefore, required by all employers.

Control of Substances Hazardous to Health (COSHH) Regulations 1999

The COSHH Regulations apply to every form of workplace and every type of work activity involving the use of substances which may be hazardous to health to people at work.

The Regulations are supported by a number of Approved Codes of Practice (ACOPS), including 'Control of substances hazardous to health', 'Control of carcinogenic substances' and 'Control of biological agents'.

Because of the relative significance of these regulations to all who use or come into contact with substances hazardous to health at work, the full extent of the duties under the regulations are covered below.

The regulations and the various ACOPs set out a strategy for safety with substances hazardous to health covering more than 40,000 chemicals and materials, together with hazardous substances generated by industrial processes.

The strategy established in the COSHH Regulations covers four main areas:

1. acquisition and dissemination of information and knowledge about hazardous substances;
2. the assessment of risks to health associated with the use, handling, storage, etc., of such substances at work;
3. elimination or control of health risks by the use of appropriate engineering applications, operating procedures and personal protection;

4.   monitoring the effectiveness of the measures taken.

It should be appreciated that the majority of the duties imposed on employers and others are of an absolute or strict nature.

Application of Regulations 6–12

Regulations 6–12 shall have effect with a view to protecting persons against risks to their health, whether immediate or delayed, arising from exposure to substances hazardous to health except:

1.   *lead* – so far as the Lead at Work Regulations 1998 apply; and *asbestos* – so far as the Control of Asbestos at Work Regulations 1987 apply;
2.   where the substances is hazardous solely by virtue of its radioactive, explosive or flammable properties, or solely because it is at a high or low temperature or a high pressure;
3.   where the risk to health is a risk to the health of a person to whom the substance is administered in the course of his medical treatment;
4.   where the substance hazardous to health is total inhalable dust which is below ground in any mine of coal.

Regulation 2 – Definitions

Approved supply list has the meaning assigned to it in regulation 4 of the Chemicals (Hazard Information and Packaging for Supply) Regulations 1994.

Biological agent means any micro-organism, cell, culture or human endoparasite, including any which have been genetically modified, which may cause any infection, allergy, toxicity or otherwise create a hazard to human health.

Carcinogen means:

1.   any *substance* or *preparation* which if classified in accordance with the classification provided by regulation 5 of the Chemicals (Hazard Information and Packaging for Supply) Regulations 1994 would be in the category of danger, carcinogenic (category 1) or carcinogenic (category 2) whether or not the substance or preparation would be required to be classified under those Regulations; or
2.   any substance or preparation:
     (a) listed in Schedule 1; and
     (b) any substance or preparation arising from a process specified in Schedule 1 which is a substance hazardous to health.

Fumigation means any operation in which a substance is released into the atmosphere so as to form a gas to control or kill pests or other undesirable organisms; and *fumigate and fumigant* shall be construed accordingly.

Maximum exposure limit for a substance hazardous to health means the maximum exposure limit approved when calculated by a method approved by the HSC.

Micro-organism includes any microbiological entity, cellular or non-cellular, which is capable of replication or of transferring genetic material.

Occupational exposure standard for a substance hazardous to health means the standard approved by the HSC for that substance in relation to the specified reference period when calculated by a method approved by the HSC.

Substance means any natural or artificial substance whether in sold or liquid form or in the form of a gas or vapour (including micro-organisms).

Substance hazardous to health means any substance (including any preparation) which is:

1. a substance which is listed in Part 1 of the approved supply list as dangerous for supply within the meaning of the Chemicals (Hazard Information and Packaging for Supply) Regulations 1994 and for which an indication of danger specified for the substance in Part V of that list is *very toxic, toxic, harmful, corrosive or irritant*;
2. a substance for which the HSC has approved a *maximum exposure limit or occupational exposure standard* (see current HSE Guidance Note EH 40 'Occupational exposure limits');
3. a *biological agent*;
4. *dust* of any kind when present at a substantial concentration in air; and
5. a substance, not being a substance mentioned in (1)–(4) above, which creates a hazard to the health of any person which is *comparable with the hazards created* by substances mentioned in (1)–(4).

Regulation 6 – Assessment of health risks created by work involving substances hazardous to health

1. An employer shall not carry on any work which is liable to expose any employees to any substance hazardous to health unless he has made a suitable and sufficient assessment of the risks created by that work to the health of those employees and of the steps that need to be taken to meet the requirements of the Regulations.
2. This assessment shall be reviewed forthwith if:
   (a) there is reason to suspect that the assessment is no longer valid; or
   (b) there has been a significant change in the work to which the assessment relates; and

(c) where as a result of the review, changes in the assessment are required, those changes shall be made.

A 'suitable and sufficient' assessment

The General ACOP indicates that a suitable and sufficient assessment should include:

1. an assessment of the risks to health;
2. the steps which need to be taken to achieve adequate control of exposure, in accordance with Regulation 7; and
3. identification of other action necessary to comply with Regulations 8–12.

An assessment of the risks created by any work should involve:

1. a consideration of:
   (a) which substances or types of substances (including micro-organisms) employees are liable to be exposed to (taking into account the consequences of possible failure of any control measures provided to meet the requirements of Regulation 7);
   (b) what effects those substances can have on the body;
   (c) where the substances are likely to be present and in what form;
   (d) the ways in which and the extent to which any groups of employees or other persons could potentially be exposed, taking into account the nature of the work and process, and any reasonably foreseeable deterioration in, or failure of, any control measure provided for the purpose of Regulation 7;
2. an estimate of exposure, taking into account engineering measures and systems of work currently employed for controlling potential exposure;
3. where valid standards exist, representing adequate control, comparison of the estimate with those standards.

Detailed guidance on COSHH assessment is provided in the HSE publication 'A step by step guide to COSHH assessment' (HMSO).

Regulation 7 – Prevention or control of exposure to substances hazardous to health

1. Every employer shall ensure that the exposure of his employees to substances hazardous to health is either prevented or, where this is not reasonably practicable, adequately controlled.
2. So far as is reasonably practicable, the prevention or adequate control of exposure of employees to substances hazardous to health, except to a carcinogen or biological agent, shall be secured by measures other than the provision of personal protective equipment.

3. Without prejudice to the generality of paragraph (1), where the assessment made under regulation 6 shows that it is not reasonably practicable to prevent exposure to a *carcinogen* by using an alternative substance or process, the employer shall employ all the following measures, namely:
   (a) the total enclosure of the process and handling systems unless this is not reasonably practicable;
   (b) the use of plant, processes and systems of work which minimise the generation of, or suppress and contain, spills, leaks, dust, fumes and vapours of carcinogens;
   (c) the limitation of the quantities of a carcinogen at the place of work;
   (d) the keeping of the number of persons exposed to a minimum;
   (e) the prohibition of eating, drinking and smoking in areas that may be contaminated by carcinogens;
   (f) the provision of hygiene measures including adequate washing facilities and regular cleaning of walls and surfaces;
   (g) the designation of those areas and installations which may be contaminated by carcinogens, and the use of suitable and sufficient warning signs; and
   (h) the safe storage, handling and disposal of carcinogens and the use of closed and clearly labelled containers.

4. Where the measures taken in accordance with paragraphs (2) or (3), as the case may be, do not prevent, or provide adequate control of, exposure to substances hazardous to health to which those paragraphs apply, then, in addition to taking those measures, the employer shall provide those employees with suitable personal protective equipment as will adequately control their exposure to those substances.

5. Any personal protective equipment provided by an employer shall comply with any enactment which implements in Great Britain any provision on design or manufacture with respect to health or safety in any relevant Community directive listed in Schedule 1 to the Personal Protective Equipment at Work Regulations 1992 which is applicable to that item of personal protective equipment.

6. Where there is exposure to a substance for which a maximum exposure limit (MEL) has been approved, the control of exposure shall, so far as the inhalation of that substance is concerned, only be treated as being adequate if the level of exposure is reduced so far as is reasonably practicable and in any case below the MEL.

7. Without prejudice to the generality of paragraph (1), where there is exposure to a substance for which an occupational exposure standard (OES) has been approved, the control of exposure shall, so far as the inhalation of the substance is concerned, only be treated as adequate if:
   (a) the OES is not exceeded; or
   (b) where the OES is exceeded, the employer identifies the reasons for

the standard being exceeded and takes appropriate action to remedy the situation as soon as is reasonably practicable.

8. Where respiratory protective equipment is provided in pursuance of this regulation, then it shall:

   (a) be suitable for the purpose; and

   (b) comply with paragraph (5) or, where no requirement is imposed by virtue of that paragraph, be of a type approved or shall conform to a standard approved, in either case, by the HSE.

9. In the event of a failure of a control measure which might result in the escape of carcinogens into the workplace, the employer shall ensure that:

   (a) only those persons who are responsible for the carrying out of repairs and other necessary work are permitted in the affected area and they are provided with suitable respiratory protective equipment and protective clothing; and

   (b) employees and other persons who may be affected are informed of the failure forthwith.

10. Schedule 3 of these Regulations shall have effect in relation to biological agents.

11. In this regulation *adequate* means adequate having regard only to the nature of the substance and the nature and degree of exposure to substances hazardous to health and *adequately* shall be construed accordingly.

Regulation 8 – Use of control measures, etc.

1. Every employer who provides any control measure, PPE or other thing or facility pursuant to these Regulations shall take all reasonable steps to ensure that it is properly used or applied as the case may be.

2. Every employee shall make full and proper use of any control measure, PPE or other thing or facility provided pursuant to these Regulations and shall take all reasonable steps to ensure it is returned after use to any accommodation provided for it and, if he discovers any defect therein, he shall report it forthwith to his employer.

Regulation 9 – Maintenance, examination and test of control measures, etc.

1. Any employer who provides any control measure to meet the requirements of Regulation 7 shall ensure that it is maintained in efficient state, in efficient working order and in good repair and, in the case of personal protective equipment, in a clean condition.

2. Where engineering controls are provided to meet the requirements of

Regulation 7, the employer shall ensure that thorough examinations and tests of those engineering controls are carried out:

(a) in the case of local exhaust ventilation (LEV) plant, at least once every fourteen months, or for LEV plant used in conjunction with a process specified in column 1 of Schedule 4, at not more than the interval specified in the corresponding entry in column 2 of that Schedule; and

(b) in any other case, at suitable intervals.

3. Where respiratory protective equipment (RPE) (other than disposable RPE) is provided to meet the requirements of Regulation 7, the employer shall ensure that at suitable intervals thorough examinations and, where appropriate, tests of that equipment are carried out.

4. Every employer shall keep a suitable record of examinations and tests carried out in accordance with the paragraphs (2) and (3), and of any repairs carried out as a result of those examinations and tests, and that record or a suitable summary thereof, shall be kept available for at least five years from the date on which it was made.

Regulation 10 – Monitoring exposure at the workplace

1. In any case in which:
    (a) it is a requisite for ensuring the maintenance of adequate control of the exposure of employees to substances hazardous to health; or
    (b) it is otherwise requisite for protecting the health of employees, the employer shall ensure that the exposure of employees to substances hazardous to health is monitored in accordance with a suitable procedure.

2. Where a substance or process is specified in column 1 of Schedule 4, monitoring shall be carried out at the frequency specified in the corresponding entry in column 2 of that Schedule.

3. The employer shall keep a suitable record of any monitoring carried out for the purpose of the regulation and that that record or a suitable summary thereof shall be kept available:
    (a) where the record is representative of the personal exposure of identifiable employees, for at least forty years;
    (b) in any other case, for at least five years.

Regulation 11 – Health surveillance

1. Where it is appropriate for the protection of the health of his employees who are, or are liable to be exposed to a substance hazardous to health, the employer shall ensure that such employees are under continuous suitable health surveillance.

2. Health surveillance shall be treated as being appropriate where:

(a) the employee is exposed to one of the substances specified in column 1 of Schedule 6 and is engaged in a process specified in column 2 of that Schedule, unless that exposure is not significant; or

(b) the exposure of the employee to a substance hazardous to health is such that an identifiable disease or adverse health effect may be related to the exposure, there is a reasonable likelihood that the disease or effect may occur under the particular conditions of his work and there are valid techniques for detecting indications of the disease or that effect.

3.   The employer shall ensure that a health record, containing particulars approved by the HSE, in respect of each of his employees to whom paragraph (1) relates is made and maintained and that that record is kept in a suitable form for at least forty years from the date of the last entry made in it.

4.   Where an employer who holds records in accordance with paragraph (3) ceases to trade, he shall forthwith notify the HSE in writing and offer those records to the HSE.

Paragraphs (5)–(12) deal with the following matters:

5. medical surveillance where employees are exposed to substances specified in Schedule 6;

6. prohibition by an employment medical adviser on engagement in work of employees considered to be at risk;

7. continuance of health surveillance for employees after exposure has ceased;

8. access by employees to their health records;

9. duty on employees to present themselves for health surveillance;

10. access to inspect a workplace or any record kept by employment medical advisers or appointed doctors;

11. review by an aggrieved employee or employer of medical suspension by an employment medical adviser or appointed doctor.

12. In this regulation:

(a) *appointed doctor* means a registered medical practitioner who is appointed for the time being in writing by the HSE for the purposes of this regulation;

(b) *employment medical adviser* means an employment medical adviser appointed under section 56 of the 1974 Act;

(c) *health surveillance* includes biological monitoring.

Regulation 12 – Information, instruction and training for persons who may be exposed to substances hazardous to health

1. An employer who undertakes work which may expose any of his employees to substances hazardous to health shall provide that employee with such information, instruction and training as is suitable and sufficient for him to know:
    (a) the risks to health created by such exposure; and
    (b) the precautions which should be taken.
2. Without prejudice to the generality of paragraph (1), the information provided under that paragraph shall include:
    (a) information on the results of any monitoring of exposure at the workplace in accordance with regulation 10 and, in particular, in the case of a substance hazardous to health specified in Schedule 1, the employee or his representatives shall be informed forthwith if the results of such monitoring shows that the MEL has been exceeded; and
    (b) information on the collective results of any health surveillance undertaken in a form calculated to prevent it from being identified as relating to a particular person.
3. Every employer shall ensure that any person (whether or not his employee) who carries out work in connection with the employer's duties under these Regulations has the necessary information, instruction and training.

Regulation 16 – Defence under the Regulations

In any proceedings for an offence consisting of a contravention of these Regulations it shall be a defence for any person to prove that he took all reasonable precautions and exercised all due diligence to avoid the commission of that offence.

Note

To rely on this defence, the employer must establish that, on the balance of probabilities, he has taken all precautions that were reasonable and exercised all due to diligence to ensure that these precautions were implemented in order to avoid such a contravention. It is unlikely that an employer could rely on a Regulation 16 defence if:

1. precautions were available which had not been taken; or
2. that he had not provided sufficient information, instruction and training, together with adequate supervision, to ensure that the precautions were effective.

Prevention and control strategies – health risks

The more important prevention and control strategies, in order of effectiveness, are:

- prohibition;
- elimination;
- substitution;
- enclosure/containment;
- isolation/separation;
- local exhaust ventilation;
- dilution ventilation;
- personal protective equipment (as the last resort).

Prevention strategies

Prohibition

In certain cases a substance may be so inherently dangerous that its use may be prohibited by law or organisation policy

Elimination

Review of the needs of specific processes can often reveal chemicals and processes which are no longer necessary.

Substitution

Can a safer material be used? There are some substances which should never be used and are proscribed in the COSHHR. Others may be banned as a matter of policy within organisations and alternatives substituted.

Control strategies

Enclosure/containment

Total enclosure or containment of the process may be made possible by the use of bulk tanks and pipework. Complete enclosure is practicable if the substances are in liquid form, used in large quantities and if the range of substances is small.

Isolation/separation

Isolation may simply mean putting the process into a small locked room, thereby separating the workforce from the risk, or could involve the construction of a chemical plant in a remote geographical area.

Ventilation systems

Ventilation is an important control strategy under the COSHHR. Here it is necessary to distinguish between natural ventilation and mechanical ventilation systems:

1. Infiltration through the fabric of a building is common. Many traditional buildings have infiltration rates of between 0.5 and 2 air changes per hour.
2. Planned natural ventilation takes place through fixed openings or vents, or through windows and doors.
3. Mechanical ventilation operates either through a system of extract fans or by means of more complex ducted ventilation systems designed to remove the contaminant at the point of emission (local exhaust ventilation). In certain cases dilution ventilation may be appropriate, or a system of air conditioning may operate.
   Infiltration and planned natural ventilation give no continuing protection wherever toxic gases, fumes, vapours, etc., are emitted from processes. Local exhaust ventilation systems must, therefore, be operated.
4. Dilution ventilation. In certain cases it may not be possible to extract a contaminant close to the point of origin. If the quantity of contaminant is small, uniformly dispersed and of low toxicity, it may be possible to dilute the contaminant by inducing large volumes of air to flow through the contaminated region. Dilution ventilation is more successfully used to control vapours, for example, organic vapours from low toxicity solvents, but is seldom successfully applied to dust and fumes, as it will not prevent inhalation.

Personal protective equipment (PPE)

Careful attention must be given to the requirements of the PPEWR and HSE Guidance accompanying the Regulations.

The use of various forms of PPE, including respiratory protective equipment, is never a perfect solution to preventing exposure to hazardous substances, however. As a control strategy it relies heavily on the operator wearing the correct PPE/RPE all the time he or she is exposed to the risk and people simply will not do this. In the majority of the cases the provision and use of PPE should be seen as an additional form of protection where other forms of protection, as indicated above, are operating.

Health and Safety at Work etc. Act 1974

Introduction

The Health and Safety at Work etc. Act 1974 (HSWA) brought in a radically new approach to dealing with the risks to people at work. The Act covers all people at work, except domestic workers in private employment.

This entry outlines the main provisions of the Act, as well as looking at issues of corporate liability and enforcement.

Objectives of the HSWA

The objectives of the Act are:

1. to secure the health, safety and welfare of all persons at work;
2. to protect others against the risks arising from workplace activities;
3. to control the obtaining, keeping and use of explosive or highly flammable substances;
4. to control emissions into the atmosphere of noxious or offensive substances.

Under the HSWA various groups of people have both specific and general duties. *All these duties are of a 'reasonably practicable' nature.*

Section 2 – General duties of employers to their employees

It is the duty of every employer, so far as is reasonably practicable, to ensure the health, safety and welfare at work of all his or her employees. This includes:

1. the provision and maintenance of plant and systems of work that are safe and without risks to health;
2. arrangements for ensuring safety and absence of risks to health in connection with the use, handling, storage and transport of articles and substances;

3. the provision of such information, instruction, training and supervision as is necessary to ensure the health and safety at work of employees;
4. the maintenance of the place of work in a condition that is safe and without risks to health and the provision and maintenance of means of access to and egress from it that are safe and without such risks;
5. the provision and maintenance of a working environment for employees that is safe, without risks to health, and adequate as regards facilities and arrangements for their welfare at work.

Employers must prepare and revise as often as is necessary, a written STATEMENT OF HEALTH AND SAFETY POLICY, and bring the Statement, and any revision of it, to the notice of all employees.

Every employer must consult appointed safety representatives with a view to making and maintaining arrangements which will enable the employer and the employees to cooperate effectively in promoting and developing measures to ensure the health and safety at work of the employees, and in checking the effectiveness of such measures.

Section 3 – General duties of employers and self-employed to persons other than their employees

Employers must conduct their undertakings in such a way as to ensure that persons not in their employment are not exposed to risks to their health and safety. (Similar duties are imposed on self-employed people.)

Employers and self-employed people must give people (not being their employees) who may be affected by the way in which they conduct their undertaking information on the way they conduct that undertaking as might affect their health and safety.

Section 4 – General duties of persons concerned with premises to persons other than their employees

This section imposes duties on employers in relation to those who:

1. are not their employees; but
2. use non-domestic premises made available to them as a place of work.

Every person who has to any extent control of premises must ensure that the premises, all means of access and exit, and any plant or substances in the premises or provided for use there, is or are safe and without risks to health.

Section 5 – General duty of persons in control of certain premises in relation to harmful emissions into the atmosphere

Any person having control of any premises of a class prescribed for the purposes of section 1(1)(d) must use the best practicable means for preventing the emission into the atmosphere from the premises of noxious or offensive substances and for rendering harmless and inoffensive such substances as may be so emitted.

Section 6 – General duties of manufacturers, etc., as regards articles and substances for use at work

Any person who designs, manufactures, imports or supplies any article for use at work:

1. must ensure that the article is so designed and constructed as to be safe and without risks to health when properly used;
2. must carry out or arrange for the carrying out of such testing and examination as may be necessary to comply with the above duty; and
3. must provide adequate information about the use for which it is designed and has been tested to ensure that, when put to that use, it will be safe and without risks to health.

Any person who undertakes the design or manufacture of any article for use at work must carry out or arrange for the carrying out of any necessary research with a view to the discovery and, so far as is reasonably practicable, the elimination or minimisation of any risks to health or safety to which the design or article may give rise.

Any person who erects or installs any article for use at work must ensure that nothing about the way it is erected or installed makes it unsafe or a risk to health when properly used.

Any person who manufactures, imports or supplies any substance for use at work:

1. must ensure that the substance is safe and without risks to health when properly used;
2. must carry out or arrange for the carrying out of such testing and examination as may be necessary; and
3. must take steps as are necessary to ensure adequate information about the results of any relevant tests is available in connection with the use of the substance at work.

Section 7 – General duties of employees at work

It is the duty of every employee while at work:

1. to take reasonable care of the health and safety of him or herself and of other persons who may be affected by his or her acts or omissions at work; and
2. as regards any duty or requirement imposed on his or her employer, to cooperate so far as is necessary to enable the duty or requirement to be performed or complied with.

Section 8 – Duty not to interfere with or misuse things provided pursuant to certain provisions

No person shall intentionally or recklessly interfere with or misuse anything provided in the interests of health, safety or welfare in pursuance of any of the relevant statutory provisions.

Section 9 – Duty not to charge employees for things done or provided pursuant to certain specific requirements

No employer shall levy, or permit to be levied, on any employee any charge in respect of anything done or provided in pursuance of any specific requirement of the relevant statutory provisions.

Corporate liability

Under the HSWA directors, managers, company secretaries and similar officers of the body corporate have both general and specific duties. Breaches of these duties can result in individuals being prosecuted.

Offences committed by companies (section 37(1))

Where a breach of one of the relevant statutory provisions on the part of a body corporate is proved to have been committed with the consent or connivance of, or to have been attributable to any neglect on the part of, any director, manager, secretary or other similar officer of the body corporate or a person who was purporting to act in any such capacity, he or she, as well as the body corporate, shall be guilty of that offence and shall be liable to be proceeded against and punished accordingly.

Generally, though, most prosecutions under section 37(1) are limited to that body of persons, i.e. the board of directors and individual functional directors, as well as senior managers.

Offences committed by other corporate persons (section 36)

Section 36 makes provision for dealing with offences committed by corporate officials, e.g. personnel managers, health and safety specialists, training officers, etc. Thus where the commission by any person of an offence under any of the relevant statutory provisions is due to the *act* or *default* of some other person, that other person shall be guilty of the offence, and a person may be charged with and convicted of the offence by virtue of this subsection whether or not proceedings are taken against the first mentioned person.

Enforcement

All modern protective legislation is based on a system of enforcement by authorised officers, such as HSE inspectors and local authority environmental health officers. Enforcement officers have powers under the specific statute, including powers of entry, the service of various forms of notice and, where appropriate, to instigate proceedings against the offender in the criminal courts.

The role of the enforcing authorities

The enforcing authorities under the Health and Safety at Work etc. Act 1974 (HSWA) are:

1. the Health and Safety Executive (HSE) which is divided into a number of specific inspectorates, e.g. Factories, Agricultural, Nuclear Installations;
2. local authorities, principally through their environmental health departments; and
3. for certain matters, the fire authority.

Actual enforcement is undertaken by inspectors appointed under the Act and authorised by a written warrant from the enforcing authority.

Powers of inspectors

Under section 20 of the HSWA an inspector has powers:

1. to enter premises at any reasonable time and, where obstruction is anticipated, to enlist the support of a police officer;
2. on entering premises,
   (a) be accompanied by any other person duly authorised by the enforcing authority; and
   (b) any equipment or materials required for any purpose for which the power of entry is being exercised;
3. to make such examination and investigation as may be necessary;
4. to direct that premises or any part of the premises, or anything in the

premises, shall remain undisturbed for so long as is reasonably necessary for the purpose of any examination or investigation;

5. to take any measurements or photographs and make any recordings as are considered necessary for the purpose of an examination or investigation;

6. to take samples of any articles or substances found in any premises, and of the atmosphere in or in the vicinity of such premises;

7. where it appears that an article or substance has caused or is likely to cause danger to health or safety, to cause it to be dismantled or subjected to any process or test;

8. to take possession of any article or substance and to detain it for so long as is necessary:
   (a) to examine it;
   (b) to ensure it is not tampered with before the examination is completed;
   (c) to ensure it is available for use as evidence in any proceedings for an offence under the relevant statutory provisions;

9. to require any person whom he or she has reasonable cause to believe to be able to give any information relevant to any examination or investigation to answer questions that the inspector thinks fit to ask and to sign a declaration of truth of the answers given;

10. to require the production of, inspect and take copies of or any entry in:
    (a) any books or documents which by virtue of the relevant statutory provisions are required to be kept; and
    (b) any other books or documents which it is necessary for the inspector to see for the purposes of any examination or investigation;

11. to require any person to afford such facilities and assistance with respect to any matters or things within that person's control or in relation to which that person has responsibilities as are necessary to enable the inspector to exercise any of the powers conferred on him or her by this section; and

12. any other power which is necessary for the purpose of carrying into effect the relevant statutory provisions.

After completing an investigation or examination, the inspector has a duty to inform the safety representatives of the matters found (section 28(8)) and must give the employer similar information.

Notices

Enforcing officers may serve two types of notice:

Improvement Notices

The Notice must state which statutory provision the inspector believes has been contravened and the reason for this belief. It should also state a time-limit within which the contravention should be remedied. (See Figure 2, p. 68.)

Prohibition Notices

A Prohibition Notice is served where there is an immediate threat to life and in anticipation of danger. This Notice directs that the specified activities in the Notice shall not be carried on, by or under the control of the person on whom the Notice is served unless certain specified remedial measures have been complied with. It should be appreciated that it is not necessary for an inspector to believe that a legal provision is being or has been contravened. (See Figure 3, p. 69.)

A Prohibition Notice may come into effect immediately after it has been served. Alternatively, it may be deferred, thereby allowing the person time to remedy the situation, carry out works, etc. The duration of a deferred Prohibition Notice is stated on the Notice.

Prosecution

Prosecution is frequently the outcome of failure to comply with an Improvement or Prohibition Notice. However, an inspector can institute legal proceedings without serving a Notice. Cases are normally heard in a magistrate's court, but for a serious offence there is provision in the HSWA on indictment to the Crown Court.

Penalties

The Offshore Safety Act 1992 amended the HSWA and empowers magistrates to impose fines of up to £20,000 for a breach of sections 2–6 of the Act, and for breach of an Improvement Notice or Prohibition Notice. The maximum fine for other offences is £5,000.

The Act also widens the range of health and safety offences for which the higher courts can impose prison sentences. The two-year maximum sentence, which existed for offences concerning explosives, licensing regimes and breach of a Prohibition Notice, is extended to cover breach of an Improvement Notice.

Health and Safety at Work, etc. Act 1974 Sections 21, 23 and 24

IMPROVEMENT NOTICE

Name and address (See Section 46)

To _____

_____

_____

(a) Delete as neccessary

(a) Trading as _____

_____

(b) Inspector's full name

I (b) _____

(c) Inspector's official designation

one of (c) _____

_____

(d) Official address

of (d) _____

Telephone

hereby give you notice that I am of the opinion that at

(e) Location of premises or place and activity

(e) _____

_____

you, as (a) an employer/a self employed person/a person wholly or partly in control of the premises, or:-

(f) Other specified activity

(f) _____

(a) are contravening/have contravened in circumstances that make it likely that the contravention will continue or be repeated/or:-

(g) Provisions contravened

(g) _____

_____

_____

The reasons for my said opinion are:-_____

_____

_____

_____

_____

_____

_____

_____

_____

_____

and I hereby require you to remedy the said conventions, or as the case may be, the matters

occassioned by them by:– (h)

(a) in the manner stated in the attached schedule which forms part of this notice.

Signature _____ Date _____

Being an Inspector appointed by an instrument in writing made pursuant to Section 19 of the said Act and entitled to issue this notice.

(a) An Improvement Notice is also being served on _____

of _____

_____

related to the matters contained in this notice.

P.S. 95059

Figure 2 Specimen Improvement Notice under the Health and Safety at Work Act (Source: HSE)

Health and Safety at Work, etc. Act 1974 Sections 21, 23 and 24

PROHIBITION NOTICE

Name and address
(See Section 46)

To _____

_____

_____

(a)   *Delete as*
    neccessary

(a) Trading as _____

(b)   *Inspector's*
    full name

I (b) _____

(c)   *Inspector's*
    official designation

one of (c) _____

(d)   *Official address*

of (d) _____

_____ Telephone _____

hereby give you notice that I am of the opinion that the following activities,

namely:– _____

_____

_____

_____

(e)   *Location of*
    activity

which are (a) being carried out by you/about to be carried out by you/under your control at (e)

_____

involve, or will involve (a) a risk/an imminent risk, of serious personal injury. I am further of the opinion that the said matters involve contraventions of the following statutory provisions:–

_____

_____

_____

because _____

_____

_____

_____

_____

and I hereby direct that the said activities shall not be carried on by you or under your control
(a) immediately/after

(f)   *Date*

(f) _____
unless the said contraventions and matters included in the schedule, which forms part of this notice,
have been remedied.

Signature _____ Date _____

Being an Inspector appointed by an instrument in writing made pursuant to Section 19 of the said Act and
entitled to issue this notice.

P.S. 95058

Figure 3 Specimen Prohibition Notice under the Health and Safety at Work Act (Source: HSE)

Human factors and safety

Introduction

Employers should recognise that the loyal, long-serving and skilled employee is their most valuable asset. Without such people many organisations would not be in business. Previous legislation, such as the Factories Act 1961, paid little attention to people at work, being concerned mainly with the safety aspects of premises and processes.

More recent legislation, namely the Management of Health and Safety at Work Regulations 1999 (MHSWR), requires a human factors-related approach to health and safety. Whereas Regulation 4 places a general duty on employers to manage their health and safety activities, Regulation 13 places an absolute duty on an employer, in entrusting tasks to his employees, to take into account their 'capabilities' as regards health and safety.

On this basis an employer may need to consider both the physical and mental capabilities of his employees in the allocation of jobs. He may need to consider, for instance, an employee's attitude towards certain safety procedures or whether an employee has the physical capability to undertake certain tasks involving, for instance, extensive manual handling operations or prolonged periods of working.

What are 'human factors'?

The Health and Safety Executive's (HSE) publication 'Human Factors in Industrial Safety' (HS(G)48) defines 'human factors' as 'a range of issues including the perceptual, physical and mental capabilities of people and the interactions of individuals with their jobs and working environments, the influence of equipment and system design on human performance and, above all, the organisation characteristics which influence safety-related behaviour at work'.

Although most health and safety legislation places the duty of compliance on the employer, this duty can only be discharged by the effective actions of the managers. Studies by the HSE's Accident Prevention Advisory Unit have shown that the vast majority of fatal accidents, and those causing major injury, could have been prevented by management action.

Areas of influence on people at work

There are three areas of influence: the organisation, the job and personal factors. These areas are each directly affected by the communication system within the organisation and the training systems and procedures in operation, all of which are directed at preventing human error.

The organisation

Those organisational characteristics which influence safety-related behaviour include:

1. the need to promote a positive climate in which health and safety are seen by management and employees as fundamental to the organisation's day-to-day operations;
2. the need to ensure that policies devised to control risks take full account of human capabilities and fallibilities;
3. commitment to the achievement of progressively higher standards, which is shown at the top of the organisation and cascaded down;
4. demonstration by senior management of their active involvement; and
5. leadership.

The job

Using techniques like job safety analysis, jobs should be designed in accordance with ergonomic principles so as to take into account limitations in human performance. Major considerations in job design include:

1. identification and comprehensive analysis of critical tasks expected of individuals, and appraisal of likely errors;
2. evaluation of required operator decision-making and the optimum balance between the human and automatic contributions to safety actions;
3. application of ergonomic principles to the design of man-machine interfaces, including displays of plant and process information, control devices and panel layouts;
4. design and presentation of procedures and operating instructions;
5. organisation and control of the working environment, including workspace, access for maintenance, noise, lighting and thermal conditions;
6. provision of correct tools and equipment;
7. scheduling of work patterns, including shift organisation, control of fatigue and stress, and arrangements for emergency operations; and
8. efficient communications, both immediate and over periods of time.

Personal factors

Personal factors, such as attitude, motivation and training, can all interact with health and safety issues.

Safety incentive schemes

These are a form of planned motivation, which can be achieved by:

1. identifying targets, which can be rewarded if fulfilled; and
2. making rewards meaningful and desirable to the people involved.

Safety incentive schemes are most effective when:

1. people are restricted to one area of activity, e.g. work in a production process;
2. measurement of safety performance is relatively simple;
3. there is regular rejuvenation or stimulation;
4. support is provided by both management and trade unions; and
5. the scheme is assisted and promoted through safety propaganda and training.

Before introducing a safety incentive scheme the following need to be considered:

1. they should be linked with some form of safety monitoring (e.g. safety inspections, safety sampling exercises);
2. they should be correct, meaningful, measurable and achievable targets should be set;
3. on no account should incentive schemes be linked with accident rates as this can discourage the reporting of accidents;
4. they tend to be shortlived and can get out of hand if not properly organised and monitored; and
5. they can shift responsibility for health and safety from management to employees and others.

Human reliability

Increasingly, attention is being paid to human error, incorrect actions or the failure to act as causative factors in accidents.

Human reliability assessment (HRA)

HRA includes the identification of all points in a sequence of operations at which incorrect human action, or the failure to act, may lead to adverse consequences for plant and/or for people. HRA techniques assign a degree of probability on a numerical scale to each event in a chain, and then, by aggregating these, arrive at an overall figure for the probability of human error for the whole chain of events.

Human errors can be classified as follows:

1. unintentional error;
2. mistakes;
3. violations;
4. skill-based errors;
5. rule-based errors;
6. knowledge-based errors.

Model for classification of error

Errors or unsafe acts can be classified as intended or unintended actions (see Figure 4, p. 76). Unintended actions can result in slips (attentional failures) and/or lapses (memory failures), both of which are largely skill-based. Intended actions are associated with mistakes, which can be either rule-based or knowledge-based, and violations as outlined above.

The significance of human capability

Human capability and the potential for error are important factors in the selection of people for different tasks. Tasks should be designed using techniques like job safety analysis, with particular reference to the various influences on behaviour that the task may produce.

Techniques based on HRA will predict the potential for human error and, linked with ergonomic principles in the design of work layouts, systems and machinery and vehicle controls and displays, should be used in the process of job design.

Human limitations likely to lead to accidents

The following features of human performance can lead to accidents:

Physical

Reach, lifting ability and capacity, skeletal features, sensory features (visual, aural), energy level.

Physiological

Illness, the effects of drugs and medication, fatigue, the oxygen supply, environmental contaminants, alcohol, time zone adjustment, ageing, the effects of the time of the day.

Psychological

Ability, aptitude, knowledge, interests, personality, memory, motivation.

Psychosocial

Cultural context, group pressures, risk taking, situational influences.

Human error

The HSE publication *Human Factors and Industrial Safety* (HS(G)48, 1989) lists a number of factors that can contribute to human error. These include:

Inadequate information

One common reason is ignorance of the production processes in which they are involved and of the potential consequences of their actions.

Lack of understanding

Often the result of a failure to communicate accurately and fully the stages of a process that an item has been through. As a result, people make presumptions that certain actions have been taken when this is not the case.

Inadequate design

Designers must always take into account human fallibility and never presume that those who operate or maintain plant or systems have a full and continuous appreciation of their essential features. Failure to consider such matters is, in itself, an aspect of human error.

Errors must be made evident or difficult, while compliance with safety precautions must be made easy. Adequate information must be provided. And systems should 'fail safe', that is, refuse to produce unsafe modes of operation.

Attention lapses

These may be due to competing demands for (limited) attention. Paradoxically, highly skilled performers may be more likely to make a slip, because they depend upon finely tuned allocation of their attention, and so avoid thinking through every minor detail.

Mistaken actions

This is the classic situation of doing the wrong thing under the impression that it is right.

Misperceptions

Misperceptions tend to occur when an individual's limited capacity to give attention to competing information under stress produces tunnel vision or when a preconceived diagnosis blocks out sources of inconsistent information.

Mistaken priorities

An organisation's objectives may not be clearly understood by individuals. When top management's goals are not clear, individuals at any level in the organisation may superimpose their own.

Wilfulness

Wilfully disregarding safety rules is rarely a primary cause of accidents. Sometimes, however, there is only a fine dividing line between mistaken priorities and wilfulness. Managers need to be alert to the influences that persuade staff to take (and condone others taking) shortcuts through the safety rules. (See Figure 4.)

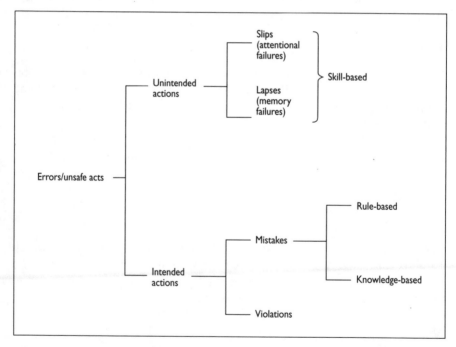

Figure 4 Classification of human error (Source: Advisory Committee on the Safety of Nuclear Installations (1991), *Second Report of the Study Group 'Human Reliability Assessment'*, HMSO, London.)

Ergonomics – the man/machine interface

Ergonomics embraces a number of disciplines including physiology, anatomy, psychology, engineering and environmental science. Fundamentally, it is concerned with maximising human performance whilst eliminating, as far as possible, the potential for human error.

Main areas for consideration

The human system

People have different physical and mental capacities, which can affect their performance. Other factors include the level of knowledge and the degree of training received, personal skills and experience of the work.

Environmental factors

The working environment, together with the need to eliminate or control environmental stressors, is an important ergonomic consideration.

The man/machine interface

The study of displays, controls and other design features of vehicles, machinery, etc., with a view to reducing operator error and stress, is a significant feature of design ergonomics. (See Figure 5.) The location, reliability, ease of operation and distinction of controls, etc., are all significant in ensuring correct operation of the various forms of work equipment.

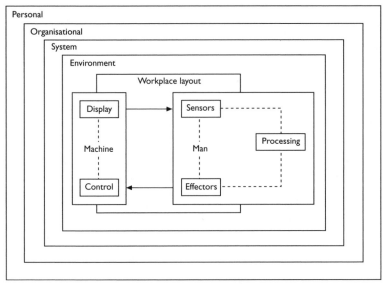

The man–machine interface

Figure 5 An integrated approach to controlling human factors

Information, instruction and training

Introduction

It is essential that employees and other persons, such as the employees of contractors, visitors and temporary workers, are adequately informed, first, of the hazards that could arise and, second, the action they may need to take to protect themselves from these hazards.

Most modern health and safety legislation requires employers to provide their employees and other persons with information, instruction and training on a wide range of issues directed at preventing accidents and work-related ill-health.

The duty to inform, instruct and train

The terms 'information', 'instruction' and 'training' are not defined in law. However, the giving of information implies the imparting of factual knowledge by one person to another. Instruction, on the other hand, involves actually telling people what to do and may incorporate an element of supervision to ensure they do it correctly. 'Training' is defined by the Department of Employment as 'the systematic development of attitude, knowledge and skill patterns required by an individual to perform adequately a given task or job'.

The duties on the part of employers and others to provide information, instruction and training to employees and other persons are incorporated in the Health and Safety at Work etc. Act 1974 (HSWA) and regulations made under the Act. In most cases, this duty is qualified by the term 'so far as is reasonably practicable'. However, under much recent legislation, such as the Management of Health and Safety at Work Regulations 1999, this duty is absolute or strict.

Health and Safety at Work etc. Act 1974

The duty to provide information, instruction and training is clearly stated thus:

Duties of employers towards employees

Every employer shall ensure the provision of such information, instruction, training and supervision as is necessary to ensure, so far as is reasonably practicable, the health and safety at work of his employees.

Duties of employers towards non-employees

The giving of information by an employer to non-employees is a matter which is not well understood by many employers. Typical examples are where contractors' employees may be working at a second employer's premises, e.g. roofing contractors, electrical contractors, or where subcontractors are working under the direction of a principal contractor. Section 3 of HSWA is quite explicit here.

It shall be the duty of every employer and every self-employed person, in the prescribed circumstances and in the prescribed manner, to give to persons (not being his employees) who may be affected by the way in which he conducts his undertaking the prescribed information about such aspects of the way in which he conducts his undertaking as might affect their health or safety.

Duties of manufacturers, etc. of articles and substances

Section 6 of the HSWA distinguishes between the duties in respect of both articles and substances, thus:

> *It shall be the duty of any person who designs, manufactures, imports or supplies any article for use at work to take such steps as are necessary to secure that there will be available in connection with the use of that article at work adequate information about the use for which it is designed and has been tested, and about any conditions necessary to ensure that, when put to that use, it will be safe and without risks to health.*
>
> *It shall be the duty of any person who manufactures, imports or supplies any substance for use at work to take such steps as are necessary to ensure that there will be available in connection with the use of that substance at work adequate information about the results of any tests which have been carried out on or in connection with the substance and about any conditions necessary to ensure that it will be safe and without risks to health when properly used.*

It should be noted that the term *article* is broadly defined as meaning:

1. any plant designed for use or operation (whether exclusively or not) by persons at work, or who erect or install any article of fairground equipment; and
2. any article designed for use as a component in any such plant or equipment.

A substance means any natural or artificial substance (including micro-organisms) intended for use (whether exclusively or not) by persons at work.

Duties under specific Regulations

Most modern health and safety legislation incorporates a duty on employers and others to provide information, instruction and training for employees and others. These legal requirements are outlined below.

Construction (Design and Management) (CDM) Regulations 1994

The CDM Regulations impose, in the main, absolute requirements and prohibitions with respect to 'construction work'. This term is very broadly defined and includes not only construction activities, such as the erection, extension or conversion of a building, but preparation for an intended structure, assembly of prefabricated elements, demolition operations and the installation of services to a structure.

There must be a formal procedure where each of those holding duties, namely clients, designers, planning supervisors, principal contractors and contractors, exchange information on a range of safety-related issues.

Control of Substances Hazardous to Health (COSHH) Regulations 1999

Where employees are liable to be exposed to a substance hazardous to health as part of their work, an employer must undertake a suitable and sufficient assessment of the risks to those employees and of the steps that need to be taken to meet the requirements of the regulations. He must then provide particular information, instruction and training as outlined below. It should be noted that this duty is extended to non-employees who are liable to be exposed.

Any employer who undertakes work which may expose any of his employees to substances hazardous to health shall provide that employee with such information, instruction and training as is suitable and sufficient for him to know:

1. the risks to health created by such exposure; and
2. the precautions which should be taken.

Without prejudice to the generality of the above paragraph, the information provided under that paragraph shall include:

1. information on the results of any monitoring of exposure at the workplace, in particular, in the case of a substance hazardous to health specified in Schedule 1, the employee or his representatives shall be

monitored forthwith if the results of such monitoring shows that the Maximum Exposure Limit has been exceeded; and

2. information on the collective results of any health surveillance under-taken in a form calculated to prevent it from being identified as relating to a particular individual.

Every employer shall ensure that any person (whether or not his employee) who carries out work in connection with the employer's duties under these regulations has the necessary information, instruction and training.

Health and Safety (Display Screen Equipment) Regulations 1992

It should be noted that these regulations apply only to defined 'users' and 'operators' of display screen equipment. A user is an employee who habit-ually uses display screen equipment as a significant part of his normal work. An *operator*, on the other hand, is a self-employed person who habitually uses display screen equipment as a significant part of his normal work.

There is an absolute duty on employers to provide training in specific situations. Where a person is an employee who does not habitually use dis-play screen equipment as a significant part of his normal work, but is to become a user in the undertaking in which he is already employed, their employer must ensure that they are provided with adequate health and safety training in the use of any workstation on which they may be required to work. Every employer must ensure that each user at work in his undertaking is provided with adequate health and safety training whenever the organisation of any workstation in that undertaking upon which he may be required to work is substantially modified.

Users must be provided with information about their daily work routine, the form of training they will receive and the measures taken by their employer to comply with his duties under the regulations, e.g. the outcome of workstation risk analysis. This duty to inform must also be read in con-junction with the general duty to provide information, which is compre-hensible, and relevant under the MSWR.

Health and Safety (Information for Employees) Regulations 1999

These regulations require information relating to health, safety and welfare to be furnished to employees by the means of posters or leaflets in the form approved and published for the purposes of the regulations by the HSE.

The poster or form is entitled *Health and safety law – What you should know* and is available from the HSE and HMSO.

Ionising Radiations Regulations 1999

The duty on the part of employers to inform, instruct and train employees and others who could be accidentally exposed to ionising radiation is a significant requirement under the regulations.

Every employer shall ensure that:

1. those employees who engaged in work with ionising radiation receive such information, instruction and training as will enable them to conduct the work in accordance with the requirements of these regulations;
2. adequate information is given to others who are directly concerned with the work with ionising radiation carried out by the employer to ensure their health and safety, so far as is reasonably practicable;
3. classified persons and trainees are informed of the health hazard, if any, associated with their work, the precautions to be taken, the importance of complying with the medical and technical requirements and given appropriate training in the field of radiation protection; and
4. those employees who are engaged in work with ionising radiation who are women are informed of the possible hazard arising from ionising radiation to the foetus in early pregnancy and the importance of informing the employer as soon as they discover they have become pregnant.

Management of Health and Safety at Work Regulations (MHSWR) 1999

Specific information, which is both comprehensible and relevant to the employees concerned, must be given to employees. What is both 'comprehensible' and 'relevant' to employees must be decided by the employer. It is inappropriate, for instance, to simply provide all employees who may be exposed to a hazardous substance with a copy of the supplier's safety data sheet. The hazards and precautions necessary in the use of the substance must be explained to them and written information must be in a style which is comprehensible to them and relevant to their operations.

The information which must be specifically provided to employees under the MHSWR is:

1. the risks to their health and safety identified by the assessment;
2. the preventive and protective measures;
3. the procedures referred to in regulation 8(1)(a) (i.e. for serious and imminent danger and for danger areas) and the measures referred to in regulation 4(2)(b) of the Fire Precautions (Workplaces) Regulations 1997 (i.e. measures for fire-fighting in the workplace);
4. the identity of those persons nominated by him in accordance with regulation 8(1)(b) (i.e. competent persons to implement procedures for serious and imminent danger and for danger areas) and regulation

4(2)(b) of the Fire Precautions (Workplaces) Regulations 1997 (i.e. persons nominated to implement measures for fire-fighting in the workplace); and

5. the risks notified to him in accordance with regulation 11(1)(c) (i.e. shared workplaces).

Information must also be provided on the procedures to be followed in an emergency and those persons designated as 'competent persons' to oversee any emergency evacuation of the workplace.

In shared workplaces, employers must exchange information on risks arising from the work and employees must be informed accordingly.

Noise at Work Regulations 1989

The regulations place the following duties on employers:

> *Every employer shall, in respect of any premises under his control, provide each of his employees who is likely to be exposed to the first action level or above or to the peak action level or above with adequate information, instruction and training on:*

1. the risk of damage to that employee's hearing that such exposure may cause;
2. what steps that employee can take to minimise the risk;
3. the steps that the employee must take in order to obtain the personal ear protectors; and
4. that employee's obligations under these regulations.

Personal Protective Equipment at Work Regulations 1992

Personal protective equipment (PPE) is defined in these regulations as meaning all equipment (including clothing affording protection against the weather) which is intended to be worn or held by a person at work and which protects him against one or more risks to his health and safety, and any addition or accessory designed to meet this objective.

Information and instruction provided to employees must be comprehensible to the those receiving same.

Employers must provide adequate and appropriate information to enable the employees to know:

1. the risk or risks that the personal protective equipment will avoid or limit;
2. the purpose for which and the manner in which the PPE is to be used; and
3. any action to be taken by the employee to ensure that the PPE remains in an efficient state, in efficient working order and in good repair.

The information and instruction provided shall not be considered adequate and appropriate unless it is comprehensible to the people to whom it is given.

Pressure Systems and Transportable Gas Containers Regulations 1989

Considerable emphasis is placed on the duties of designers and suppliers of pressure systems to provide very comprehensive information to the users of such systems.

Designers and suppliers of pressure systems must provide sufficient information concerning the design, construction, examination, operation and maintenance of pressure systems as may reasonably foreseeably be needed to enable the provisions of the regulations to be complied with.

Similar requirements apply in the case of employers of those who modify or repair pressure systems.

Provision and Use of Work Equipment Regulations 1998

The duty to provide information, instruction and training under these regulations is extensive and must cover safe use of the equipment, foreseeable abnormal situations in the use of the equipment and remedial action necessary, and any conclusions to be drawn from experience in previous use of the equipment.

Every employer shall ensure that all those who use work equipment have available to them adequate health and safety information and, where appropriate, written instructions pertaining to the use of that equipment.

Again, such information provided to employees must be comprehensible to those employees.

Every employer shall ensure that any of his employees who supervise or manage the use of work equipment has available to him similar adequate information.

The information and instructions required by either of the above paragraphs shall include information and, where appropriate, written instructions on:

1. the conditions in which and the methods by which the work equipment may be used;
2. foreseeable abnormal situations and the action to be taken if such a situation were to occur; and
3. any conclusions to be drawn from experience in using the work equipment.

Information and instructions required by this regulation shall be readily comprehensible to those concerned.

Safety Representatives and Safety Committees Regulations 1977

Trade union-appointed safety representatives are entitled to a wide range of information under these regulation. An employer must make available to safety representatives the information within the employer's knowledge necessary to them to enable them to fulfil their functions except:

1. any information the disclosure of which would be against the interest of national security;
2. any information that they could not disclose without contravening a prohibition imposed by or under any enactment;
3. any information relating specifically to an individual, unless he has consented to it being disclosed;
4. any information the disclosure of which would, for reasons other than its effect on health, safety or welfare at work, cause substantial injury to the employer's undertaking or, where the information was supplied to them by some other person, to the undertaking of that other person; and
5. any information obtained by the employer for the purpose of bringing, prosecuting or defending any legal proceedings.

Legislation

Introduction

Health and safety law originated with the industrial revolution and the appalling conditions in which some people worked during the nineteenth century. It is based on both common law precedents (the unwritten law) and statutes, such as the Health and Safety at Work etc. Act 1974 (HSWA) (the written law). In many cases, common law precedents form the basis for subsequent statute law.

A breach of the HSWA, together with any Regulations made under the same, mainly gives rise to criminal liability. This means that an offender can be brought before the criminal courts and, if found guilty, fined or imprisoned, or both.

On the other hand, a breach of common law, in particular the tort of negligence, may result in a civil claim being made by the injured party (the plaintiff) against another individual (the defendant). (A 'tort' is defined as a civil wrong and the law of tort is a specific branch of the law.) In this case, the normal remedy would be an award of damages based on the severity of injury, damage or loss sustained by the plaintiff. (See Figures 6 and 7, pp. 88, 89.)

Common law

Common law is based on court judgments which have been bound by the doctrine of precedent into a body of authoritative principles and rules. It accounts for the greater part of the law of contract and tort, both of which have played a significant role in the development of civil liability relating to occupational health and safety.

The main contribution of common law to health and safety law is the body of rules developed in connection with the right of employees and their dependants to sue employers for damages for personal injury, disease or death at work, i.e. the civil liability of employers is to be found mainly in the rules of tort.

Common law duties of the employer

Under common law employers must take reasonable care to protect their

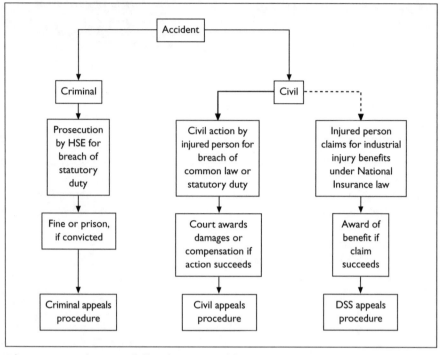

Figure 6 Legal routes following an accident

employees from risk of foreseeable injury, disease or death at work. The effect of this requirement is that if an employer knows, or ought to have known, of a health and safety risk to employees, he or she will be liable if an employee is injured or killed, or suffers illness as a result of the risk, or if the employer failed to take reasonable care.

An employer's duties in common law were identified in general terms by the House of Lords in *Wilsons & Clyde Coal Co. Ltd* v *English* (1938) AC 57. The common law requires that all employers provide and maintain:

1. a safe place of work with safe means of entry and exit;
2. safe appliances and equipment and plant for doing the work;
3. a safe system for doing the work; and
4. competent and safety-conscious personnel.

These duties apply even though an employee may be working on third party premises, or where an employee has been hired out to another employer, but where the control of the task he is performing remains with the permanent employer. The test of whether an employee has been temporarily 'employed' by another employer is one of 'control'.

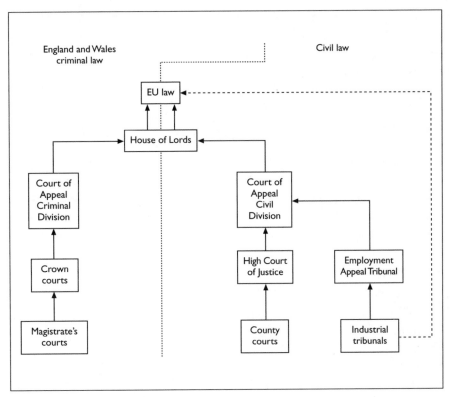

Figure 7 Courts structure

The tort of negligence

The common law duties of employers listed above are part of the general law of negligence and, as such, are specific aspects of the duty to take reasonable care.

Negligence is defined as:

1. the existence of a duty of care owed by the defendant to the plaintiff;
2. breach of that duty; and
3. damage, loss or injury resulting from or caused by that breach *(Lochgelly Iron & Coal Co. Ltd* v *M'Mullan* (1934) AC 1).

These three facts must be established by an injured employee before he or she is entitled to bring a claim for damages though, in the case of breach of statutory duty, he or she merely has to show that the breach of that statutory duty was the material cause of his injury. It is essential that the breach of duty caused the injury or occupational disease. Breach of duty need not be the exclusive cause, but it must be a substantial one, i.e. it must materially contribute to the injury or ill-health condition.

The legal process involving the tort of negligence is for a plaintiff to sue a defendant for damages.

Criminal law

A crime can result in prosecution by an official body, such as the Police or Health and Safety Executive (HSE). Criminal cases are heard in the magistrate's courts in England and Wales or for more serious cases in the Crown Court.

The main sanctions a criminal court can impose are a fine and/or imprisonment. Compensation may be ordered, however, for an individual to cover personal injury and damage to property, but a compensation order is not available to dependants of a deceased person in consequence of his or her death.

Civil law

This area of the law is concerned with civil liability arising from an act or omission which the law regards as giving one individual, company or organisation the right to present a legal claim against another. Civil claims are heard in the civil courts, principally the County Courts or the High Court.

The two areas of civil law most relevant to health and safety at work are *torts*, a collective name for certain rights of action, especially negligence and breach of statutory duty, and *breach of contract*.

Civil liability in tort can be insured against, and such insurance against liability is compulsory for most classes of employers.

Contract law

A contract law is an agreement between two parties. To be legally enforceable it must:

* consist of an offer made by one party which must be accepted unconditionally by the other;
* have a consideration that flows from one party to the other (this is the legal ingredient that changes an informal agreement into a legally binding contract);
* the parties must intend to enter into a legally binding agreement; and
* both parties must have the legal capacity to make such a contract. (Capacity to contract means that the parties must be sane, sober and over the age of 18 as a rule.)

Statutes, Regulations, Approved Codes of Practice and Guidance Notes

Statutes

These are Acts of Parliament, e.g. Factories Act 1961, Offices, Shops and Railway Premises Act 1963, Health and Safety at Work etc. Act 1974 (HSWA).

Regulations

Most statutes give the minister(s) power to make Regulations (subordinate or delegated legislation) without referring the matter to Parliament. The Regulations may be drafted by the HSE and submitted through the Health and Safety Commission (HSC) to the secretary of state or minister, e.g. Control of Substances Hazardous to Health Regulations 1999 (COSHHR), Noise at Work Regulations 1989, Safety Representatives and Safety Committees Regulations 1977, and Management of Health and Safety at Work Regulations 1999(MHSWR).

There is a general requirement for the HSC and HSE to keep interested parties informed of, and adequately advised on, such matters.

Approved Codes of Practice (ACOPs)

The need to provide guidance on Regulations is recognised in section 16 of the HSWA, which gives the HSC power to prepare and approve Codes of Practice on matters contained not only in Regulations but also in sections 2–7 of the Act. Before approving a Code, the HSE acting for the HSC, must consult with any interested body.

An ACOP is a quasi-legal document. Although non-compliance does not constitute a breach, if the contravention of the Act or Regulations is alleged, the fact that the ACOP was not followed would be accepted in court as evidence of failure to do all that was reasonably practicable. A defence would be to prove that works of equivalent nature had been carried out or that something equally good or better had been done.

HSE Guidance Notes

The HSE issues Guidance Notes in some cases to supplement information in ACOPs. Guidance Notes have no legal status and are of an advisory nature only.

The hierarchy of duties

Statutory duties give rise to criminal liability. This means that an offender can be prosecuted by the enforcement agencies and brought before a court to answer the alleged offences. There are three distinct levels of statutory duty, namely those of an absolute or strict nature, and those qualified by the terms 'practicable', 'reasonably practicable' and 'reasonable'. The significance of these terms must be appreciated in the interpretation of health and safety law.

'Absolute' requirements

Where risk of injury or disease is inevitable if safety requirements are not followed, a statutory duty may well be strict or absolute. Absolute duties are qualified by the terms 'shall' or 'must', and there is little or no defence available when charged with such an offence.

Most of the new duties under the MHSWR, the Workplace (Health, Safety and Welfare) Regulations 1992 (WHSWR) and the Provision and Use of Work Equipment Regulations 1998 (PUWER) are of an absolute nature, which implies a higher level of duty than that of other legislation, such as the Factories Act 1961 and the HSWA 1974.

'Practicable' requirements

A statutory requirement qualified by the term 'so far as is practicable' implies that if in the light of current knowledge and invention it is feasible to comply with this requirement then, irrespective of the cost or sacrifice involved, such a requirement must be complied with (*Schwalb* v *Fass (H) & Son* (1946)175 LT 345). Thus, 'practicable' means more than physically possible and implies a higher duty of care than a duty qualified by the term 'so far as is reasonably practicable'.

'Reasonably practicable' requirements

A duty qualified by the term 'so far as is reasonably practicable' implies a lower or lesser level of duty than one which is qualified by 'so far as is practicable'. 'Reasonably practicable' is a narrower term than 'physically possible' (i.e. 'practicable'), and implies that a computation must be made in which the quantum of risk is placed in one scale and the sacrifice involved in the measures necessary for averting that risk is placed in the other. Most duties under the HSWA are qualified by the term 'so far as is reasonably practicable'.

The reasonable man

A further level of duty is qualified by the term 'reasonable'. The term is flexible and changes over time according to society and the norms prevalent at the time.

Tribunals

Employment tribunals (formerly industrial tribunals) were first established under the Industrial Training Act 1964 to deal with appeals against industrial training levies by employers. They now cover many industrial matters, for example, industrial relations issues, and cases involving unfair dismissal, equal pay and sex discrimination. Each tribunal consists of a legally qualified chairman appointed by the Lord Chancellor and two lay members, one from management and one from a trade union, selected from panels maintained by the Department of Employment following nominations from employers' organisations and trade unions. However, since 1999, anyone has been able to offer themselves for appointment. This will mean that some tribunals will no longer represent the traditional 'sides' of industry (although such perceived polarisation seldom occurs in practice).

When all three members of a tribunal are sitting the majority view prevails.

Complaints relating to health and safety matters

Employment tribunals deal with the following employment/health and safety issues:

1. appeals against improvement and prohibition notices served by enforcement officers;
2. time off for the training of safety representatives (Safety Representatives and Safety Committees Regulations 1977, Reg. 11(1)(a));
3. failure of an employer to pay a safety representative for time off for undertaking his functions and training (Safety Representatives and Safety Committees Regulations 1977, Reg. 11(1)(b));
4. failure of an employer to make a medical suspension payment (Employment Protection (Consolidation) Act 1978, section 22); and
5. actual or constructive dismissal following a breach of health and safety law, regulation and/or term of employment contract.

Management of health and safety

Introduction

'Management' may be defined as 'the efficient use of resources in the pursuit of organisational goals'. As with any other aspect of an organisation's management activities, such as finance, production, engineering and distribution, there must be a clearly defined system and arrangements for managing health and safety. The organisation's STATEMENT OF HEALTH AND SAFETY POLICY should be seen as the starting point of this process.

Earlier legislation, such as the Factories Act 1961 and Offices, Shops and Railway Premises Act 1963, mainly laid down minimum prescriptive standards that employers were required to comply with. The need for management systems, however, was implied in the Health and Safety at Work etc. Act 1974.

Under the Management of Health and Safety at Work Regulations 1999 employers must undertake 'a suitable and sufficient assessment of the risks' to their employees and other persons affected by the activities of their undertaking. Having completed the risk assessment process, employers must, further, effect arrangements for *the effective planning, organisation, control, monitoring and review* of the preventive and protective measures arising from the risk assessment. These 'arrangements' must be recorded in most cases.

A number of management systems are available for consideration by employers and are incorporated below.

Accidents and ill-health at work

The term 'accident' may be defined as 'an unexpected unplanned event in a series of events that occurs through a combination of causes. It results in physical harm (injury or disease) to an individual, damage to property, business interruption, or any combination of these effects'.

Forms of injury and damage to health

Injuries

Injuries can take a number of forms:

- fatal;
- fractures of bones;
- amputations;
- loss of sight;
- loss of consciousness;
- cuts, abrasions, lacerations.

Occupational diseases and conditions

These may be of a physical, chemical, biological or work-induced origin.

The cost of accidents and ill-health

Accidents resulting in death, major injury and lost time, together with ill-health arising from work activities, represent a substantial loss to organisations. (See ACCIDENTS AND INJURIES.)

The duty to manage health and safety at work

The Management of Health and Safety at Work Regulations (MHSWR) 1999 place a strict duty on employers to actually manage the health and safety of their employees, as opposed to merely complying with minimum legal requirements. This duty is directly connected with the duty on employers to undertake a suitable and sufficient assessment of the risks to both employees and non-employees. Fundamentally, a risk assessment should identify the management systems necessary 'to comply with the requirements and prohibitions imposed by or under the relevant statutory provisions'. (See RISK ASSESSMENT.)

In the case of young persons (i.e. persons between the ages of 16 and 18 years), an employer shall not employ a young person unless he has, in relation to the health and safety of young persons, made or reviewed an assessment in accordance with the above duty and specific factors relating to young persons.

Regulation 4 specifies the principles of prevention to be applied. thus, where an employer implements any preventive and protective measures, he shall do so on the basis of the principles specified in Schedule 1 (General Principles of Prevention) to the Regulations. The general principles of prevention are:

1. avoiding risks;

2. evaluating the risks which cannot be avoided;
3. combating the risks at source;
4. adapting the work to the individual, especially as regards the design of workplaces, the choice of work equipment and the choice of working and production methods, with a view, in particular, to alleviating monotonous work and work at a predetermined work rate and to reducing their effects on health;
5. adapting to technical progress;
6. replacing the dangerous by the non-dangerous;
7. developing a coherent overall prevention policy which covers technology, organisation of work, working conditions, social relationships and the influence of factors relating to the working environment;
8. giving collective protective measures priority over individual protective measures; and
9. giving appropriate instructions to employees.

The duty to manage health and safety at work is firmly established in Regulation 5 thus:

1. Every employer shall make and give effect to such arrangements as are appropriate having regard to the nature of his activities and the size of his undertaking, for the effective *planning, organisation, control, monitoring and review* of the preventive and protective measures.
2. Where the employer employs five or more employees, he shall record the arrangements referred to in paragraph L.

These 'arrangements' might be recorded, perhaps, in the form of a series of in-house codes of practice incorporated in an organisation's Health and Safety Manual. Procedures for ensuring effective compliance, for establishing performance objectives and for measuring actual performance against agreed objectives, should also be established.

The Approved Code of Practice, which accompanies the MHSWR, expands on the above requirements as follows:

Planning

Adopting a systematic approach that identifies priorities and sets objectives. Whenever possible, risks are eliminated by the careful selection and design of facilities, equipment and processes or minimised by the use of physical control measures.

Organisation

Putting in place the necessary structure with the aim of ensuring that there is progressive improvement in health and safety performance.

Control

Ensuring that the decisions for ensuring and promoting health and safety are being implemented as planned.

Monitoring and review

Like quality, progressive improvements in health and safety can only be achieved through the constant development of policies, approaches to implementation and techniques of risk control.

This pro-active approach is one which organisations must consider, sooner than a merely reactive response following accidents or ill-health associated with work activities.

Management systems

Management systems that need consideration and implementation in order to ensure compliance with duties under the regulations include:

1. risk assessment procedures for the workplace, work equipment, personal protective equipment, manual handling operations and work with display screen equipment; other risk assessments dealing with, for instance, dangerous activities, such as entry into confined spaces, may also be necessary;
2. planned preventive maintenance of the workplace, work equipment, systems and safety devices;
3. the development and implementation of cleaning schedules;
4. the development and operation of emergency procedures;
5. where staff may be exposed to risks to their health identified by the risk assessment, the implementation of health surveillance for such staff;
6. the appointment and training of competent persons to assist the employer in both ensuring compliance with legal requirements and for implementing emergency procedures. (See COMPETENT PERSONS.)
7. on-going health and safety training of staff generally, but particularly
   (a) on recruitment (i.e. induction training);
   (b) on being exposed to new or increased risks through job transfer or change of responsibilities, the introduction of new work equipment, changes in existing work equipment, introduction of new technology, new system of work or change in an existing system of work;
8. human capability assessment with regard to health and safety aspects of jobs;
9. procedures for providing health and safety information;
10. the safety regulation of contractors on site and of employees who may be operating away from base; and

11. procedures for consultation with trade union safety representatives and representatives of employee safety. (See REPRESENTATION.)

Successful health and safety management

The HSE publication *Successful Health and Safety Management* (HS(G)65) specifies five essential elements necessary in the successful management of health and safety thus:

1. the establishment of policy and successful development of policy;
2. establishing and developing the organisation and arrangements for implementing the policy;
3. planning strategies and implementation of those strategies to eliminate or control risks;
4. measuring performance of managers against agreed health and safety objectives;
5. reviewing management performance.

Various forms of health and safety monitoring (see MONITORING SYSTEMS), such as safety audits and inspections, should result in feedback for policy revision and review. These elements are summarised in Figure 8.

BS 8800: 1996 – Guide to Occupational Health and Safety Management Systems

In recent years many organisations have adopted the ISO 9000 series of quality standards. Moreover, the introduction of the ISO 14001 and ISO 14004 environmental management systems prompted the introduction of a comparable standard in occupational health and safety management. The resulting BS 8800 provides the procedure for an organisation to review and revise its current occupational health and safety arrangements against a standard that has been developed by industry, commerce, insurers, regulators, trade unions and occupational health and safety practitioners.

Review elements

When undertaking a review of current arrangements, the following headings should be considered:

1. requirements of relevant legislation dealing with the occupational health and safety management issues;
2. existing guidance on occupational health and safety management available within the organisation;
3. best practice and performance in the organisation's employment sector and other appropriate sectors;

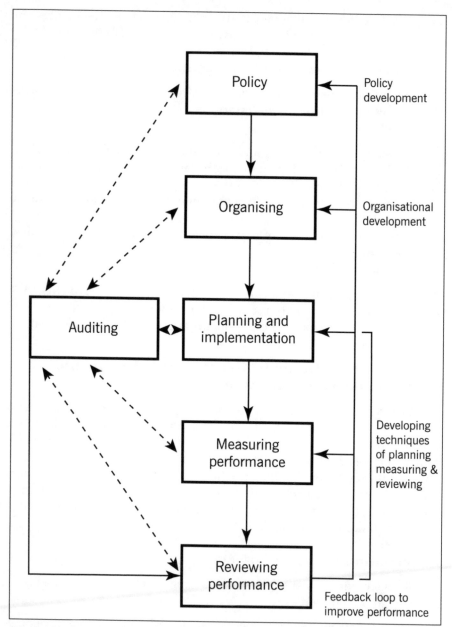

Figure 8 Key elements of successful health and safety management

------------► Information link

————————► Control link

(Source: HSE (1997) *Successful Health and Safety Management*, HMSO, London.)

4. efficiency and effectiveness of existing resources devoted to occupational health and safety management.

Effective statements of health and safety policy

BS 8800 lists nine policy elements which indicate the status of occupational health and safety management within an organisation. These principal elements are:

1. recognising that occupational health and safety management is an integral part of its business performance;
2. achieving a high level of occupational health and safety performance, with compliance to legal requirements as the minimum, and continual cost-effective improvement in performance;
3. providing adequate and appropriate resources to implement the policy;
4. the setting and publishing of occupational health and safety objectives, even if only by internal notification;
5. placing the management of occupational health and safety as a prime responsibility of line management, from most senior executive to first-line supervisory level;
6. ensuring the statement's understanding, implementation and maintenance at all levels in the organisation;
7. ensuring employee involvement and consultation to gain commitment to the policy and its implementation;
8. periodic review of the policy, the management system and audit of compliance to policy;
9. ensuring that employees at all levels receive appropriate training and are competent to carry out their duties and responsibilities.

(See also STATEMENTS OF HEALTH AND SAFETY POLICY.)

Further guidance is provided in BS 8800.

The right safety culture

All organisations incorporate a set of cultures, which have developed over a period of time. They are associated with the accepted standards of behaviour within that organisation, and the development of a specific culture with regard to quality, customer service and written communications is a continuing quest for many organisations.

With the greater emphasis on health and safety management under the MHSWR, attention must be paid to the establishment and development of an appropriate safety culture within the organisation. Both the Health and Safety Executive and Confederation of British Industry provide guidance on this issue.

The main principles are:

1. the acceptance of responsibility at and from the top, exercised through a clear chain of command, seen to be actual and felt throughout the organisation;
2. a conviction that high standards are achievable through proper management;
3. setting and monitoring of relevant objectives/targets, based upon satisfactory internal information systems;
4. systematic identification and assessment of hazards and the devising and exercise of preventive systems which are subject to audit and review; in such approaches, particular attention is paid to the investigation of error;
5. immediate rectification of deficiencies; and
6. promotion and reward of enthusiasm and good results.

(See Figure 9.)

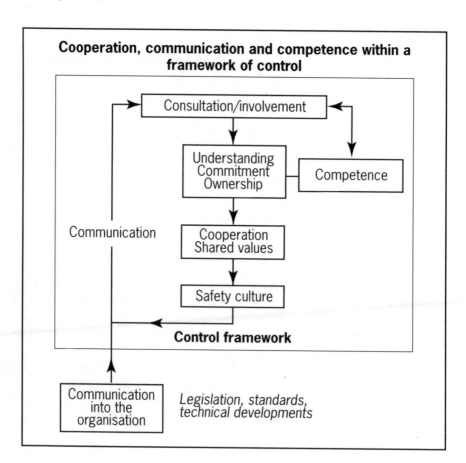

Management of Health and Safety at Work Regulations 1999

Introduction

These Regulations represent a significant change in the approach to health and safety law, and are accompanied by an Approved Code of Practice (ACOP). As such, they require a more management-oriented approach to compliance with health and safety LEGISLATION generally. Duties on individuals are of an absolute or strict nature, compared with those under the Health and Safety at Work etc Act and other Regulations where the duties are qualified by the term 'so far as is practicable' or 'so far as is reasonably practicable'.

   The Management of Health and Safety at Work Regulations implemented the European Framework Directive 'on the introduction of measures to encourage improvements in the safety and health of workers at work'. The Framework Directive was accompanied by five Daughter Directives dealing with the workplace, work equipment, personal protective equipment, manual handling and display screen equipment. These Directives were implemented in the UK as:

- The Workplace (Health, Safety and Welfare) Regulations 1992
- The Provision and Use of Work Equipment Regulations 1998
- The Personal Protective Equipment at Work Regulations 1992
- The Manual Handling Operations Regulations 1992
- The Health and Safety (Display Screen Equipment) Regulations 1992

The more detailed provisions of the above regulations, and other Regulations, such as the Lifting Operations and Lifting Equipment Regulations (LOLER) 1998 and Part II of the Fire Precautions (Workplaces) Regulations (FPWR) 1997, must be read in conjunction with the general provisions of the MSWR.

Principal requirements

The principal requirements of the MSWR are outlined below.

Regulation 3 – Risk assessment

This regulation places an absolute duty on every employer to make a suitable and sufficient assessment of the risks to the health and safety of:

1. his employees to which they are exposed whilst at work; and
2. persons not in his employment arising out of or in connection with the conduct by him of his undertaking,

for the purpose of identifying the measures he needs to take to comply with the requirements and prohibitions imposed upon him by or under the *relevant statutory provisions* and by Part II of the FM 1997.

Relevant statutory provisions

These are the provisions of the statute, i.e. the HSWA, and of any Regulations made under the statute, e.g. Noise at Work Regulations 1989.

Regulation 4 – Principles of prevention to be applied

Where an employer implements preventive and protective measures he shall do so on the basis of the principles specified in Schedule 1 to the Regulations.

Regulation 5 – Health and safety arrangements

This regulation places an absolute duty on employers to actually manage their health and safety-related activities thus:

> *Every employer shall make and give effect to such arrangements as are appropriate, having regard to the nature of his activities and the size of his undertaking, for the* effective planning, organisation, control, monitoring and review *of the preventive and protective measures.*

These arrangements must be recorded where five or more employees are employed.

Regulation 6 – Health surveillance

Every employer shall ensure that his employees are provided with such health surveillance as is appropriate having regard to the risks to their health and safety which are identified by the assessment.

Regulation 7 – Health and safety assistance

An employer must appoint one or more *competent persons* to assist him in undertaking the measures he needs to take to comply with the requirements and prohibitions imposed upon him by or under the relevant statutory provisions and by Part II of the FPWR 1997.

This regulation does not apply to self-employed persons and those carrying on a business in partnership where that person or a partner respectively has sufficient training or experience or knowledge as to be considered competent.

Regulation 8 – Procedures for serious and imminent danger and for danger areas

Employers must:

1. establish and where necessary give effect to appropriate procedures to be followed in the event of serious or imminent danger to persons at work;
2. nominate a sufficient number of *competent persons* to implement these procedures;
3. prevent any employee being given access to a danger area unless he has received adequate health and safety instruction.

Regulation 9 – Contacts with external services

Every employer shall ensure that any necessary contacts with external services are arranged, particularly as regards first aid, emergency medical care and rescue work.

Regulation 10 – Information for employees

Every employer shall provide his employees with *comprehensible and relevant* information on:

1. the risks to their health and safety identified by the assessment;
2. the preventive and protective measures;
3. the procedures referred to in regulation 8(1)(a) and the measures referred to in regulation 4(2)(a) of the FPWA 1997;
4. the identity of the competent persons nominated in accordance with regulation 8(1)(b) and the measures referred to in regulation 4(2)(b) of the PWR 1997; and
5. the risks notified to him in accordance with regulation 11(1)(c) (shared workplaces).

Every employer shall, before employing a child, provide a parent of the child with comprehensible and relevant information on:

1. the risks to his health and safety identified by the assessment;
2. the preventive and protective measures; and
3. the risks notified in accordance with Regulation 11(1)(c).

Regulation 11 – Cooperation and coordination

This regulation concerns the duties of employers who share workplaces, whether on a temporary basis, e.g. a construction site, or a permanent basis, e.g. office block, industrial estate. Each employer must:

1. cooperate with other employers to enable them to comply with legal requirements;
2. take all reasonable steps to coordinate the measures he is taking with other employers in order to comply with legal requirements; and
3. take all reasonable steps to inform other employers of risks to their employees' health and safety arising from his activities.

In particular, these duties should be read in conjunction with the requirements under the Construction (Design and Management) Regulations 1994 where a construction project may involve several employers.

Regulation 12 – Persons working in host employers or self-employed persons' undertakings

This regulation covers the situation where employees of another employer may be working in an employer's premises, business activity or operation. it largely extends the duties under section 3 of HSWA with regard to the giving by employers of information, instruction and training to non-employees working on their premises or in their business activity.

Thus every employer and self-employed person shall ensure that the employer of any employees from an outside undertaking who are working in his undertaking is provided with comprehensible information on:

1. the risks arising in the undertaking; and
2. the measures taken by the first mentioned employer to comply with legal requirements and to protect those employees.

These measures include details of emergency and evacuation procedures and the competent persons nominated to implement such procedures.

Regulation 13 – Capabilities and training

Every employer shall, in entrusting tasks to his employees, take into account their capabilities as regards health and safety.

This requirement implies a need to match the individual to the task, both mentally and physically, from a health and safety viewpoint. It requires a good understanding of the human factors aspect of health and safety, in particular ergonomic considerations, the physical and mental limitations of people and the potential for human error.

Regulation 13(2) deals with training issues and actually specifies situations where there is an absolute duty to ensure the provision of health and safety training. Thus:

Every employer shall ensure that his employees are provided with adequate health and safety training:

1. on their being recruited into the employer's undertaking;
2. on their being exposed to new or increased risks because of:
   (a) their being transferred or given a change of responsibilities within the employer's undertaking;
   (b) the introduction of new work equipment into or a change respecting work equipment already in use within the employer's undertaking;
   (c) the introduction of new technology into the employer's undertaking; or
   (d) the introduction of a new system of work or a change respecting a system of work already in use within the employer's undertaking.

Training shall:

1. be repeated periodically where appropriate;
2. be adapted to take account of new or changed risks; and
3. take place during working hours.

Regulation 14 – Employees' duties

Every employee shall use any machinery, equipment, dangerous substance, transport equipment, means of production of safety device provided to him by his employer in accordance both with any training in the use of the equipment concerned which has been received by him and the instructions respecting that use which have been provided to him by the said employer in compliance with the requirements and prohibitions imposed upon that employer by or under the relevant statutory provisions.

Every employee shall inform his employer or any other employee with specific responsibility for the health and safety of his fellow employees (e.g. competent person, trade union safety representative):

1. of any work situation which a person with the first-mentioned employee's training and instruction would reasonably consider represented a serious and immediate danger to health and safety; and
2. of any matter which a person with the first-mentioned employee's training and instruction would reasonably consider represented a shortcoming in the employer's protection arrangements for health and safety.

Regulation 15 – Temporary workers

This regulation places an absolute duty on employers to provide any person working under a fixed term contract of employment or employed in an employment business with comprehensible information on:

1. any special occupational qualifications or skills required to be held by that employee if he is to carry out his work safely; and
2. of any health surveillance required, before the employee concerned commences his duties.

Further provisions apply in the case of persons carrying an employment business being required to pass on information to the employees concerned before working in another employer's undertaking.

Regulation 16 – Risk assessment in respect of new or expectant mothers

Where:

1. the persons working in an undertaking include women of child-bearing age; and
2. the work is of a kind which could involve risk, by reason of her condition, to the health and safety of a new or expectant mother, or to that of her baby, from any processes or working conditions, or physical, biological or chemical agents,

the assessment required by regulation 3(1) shall also include an assessment of such risk. Where, in the case of an individual employee, the taking of any other action the employer is required to take under the relevant statutory provisions would not avoid the risk referred to above, the employer shall, if it is reasonable to do so, and would avoid such risks, alter her working conditions or hours of work.

If it is not reasonable to alter working conditions or hours of work, or if it would not avoid such risk, the employer shall, subject to section 67 of the Employment Rights Act (ERA 1996, suspend the employee from work so long as is necessary to avoid such risk.

References to risk, in relation to risk from any infectious or contagious disease, are references to a level of risk which is in addition to the level to which a new or expectant mother may be expected to be exposed outside the workplace.

Regulation 17 – Certificate from a registered medical practitioner in respect of new or expectant mothers

Where:

1. a new or expectant mother works at night; and
2. a certificate from a registered medical practitioner or a registered midwife shows that it is necessary for her health or safety that she should not be at work for any period of such work identified in the certificate;

the employer shall, subject to section 67 of the ERA 1996, suspend her from work so long as is necessary for her health or safety.

Regulation 18 – Notification by new or expectant mothers

Nothing in paragraph 2 or 3 of Regulation 16 shall require the employer to take any action in relation to an employee until she has notified the employer in writing that she is pregnant, has given birth within the previous six months, or is breastfeeding.

Nothing in paragraph 2 or 3 of Regulation 16 or in Regulation 17 shall require the employer to maintain action taken in relation to an employee:

1. in a case:
   (a) to which regulation 16(2) or (3) relates; and
   (b) where the employee has notified her employer that she is pregnant, where she has failed, within a reasonable time of being requested to do so in writing by her employer, to produce for the employer's inspection a certificate from a registered medical practitioner or a registered midwife showing that she is pregnant;
2. once the employer knows that she is no longer a new or expectant mother; or
3. if the employer cannot establish whether she remains a new or expectant mother.

Regulation 19 – Protection of young persons

Every employer shall ensure that young persons employed by him are protected at work from any risks to their health or safety which are a consequence of their lack of experience, or absence of awareness of existing or potential risks or the fact that young persons have not yet fully matured.

Subject to paragraph 3, no employer shall employ a young person for work:

1. which is beyond his physical or psychological capacity;
2. involving harmful exposure to agents which are toxic or carcinogenic, cause heritable genetic damage or harm to the unborn child or which in any other way chronically affect human health;
3. involving harmful exposure to radiation;
4. involving the risk of accidents which it may reasonably be assumed cannot be recognised or avoided by young persons owing to their insufficient attention to safety or lack of experience or training; or

5. in which there is a risk to health from:
    (a) extreme cold or heat;
    (b) noise; or
    (c) vibration,

    and in determining whether work will involve harm or risks for the purpose of this paragraph, regard shall be had to the results of the assessment.

Nothing in paragraph 2 shall prevent the employment of a young person who is no longer a child for work:

1. where it is necessary for his training;
2. where the young person will be supervised by a competent person; and
3. where any risk will be reduced to the lowest level that is reasonably practicable.

Regulation 21 – Provisions as to liability

Nothing in the relevant statutory provisions shall operate so as to afford an employer a defence in criminal proceedings for a contravention of those provisions by reason of any act or default of:

1. an employee of his; or
2. a person appointed by him under Regulation 7 (competent person).

Regulation 22 – Exclusion of civil liability

Breach of a duty imposed by these Regulations shall not confer a right of action in any civil proceedings.

Table 3 MHSWR 1999: Schedule 1

GENERAL PRINCIPLES OF PREVENTION
This Schedule specifies the general principles of prevention set out in Article 6(2) of Council Directive 89/391/EEC thus:

(a) avoiding risks;

(b) evaluating the risks which cannot be avoided;

(c) combating the risks at source;

(d) adapting the work to the individual, especially as regards the design of workplaces, the choice of work equipment and the choice of working and production methods, with a view, in particular, to alleviating monotonous work and work at a predetermined work rate and reducing their effect on health;

(e) adapting to technical progress;

(f) replacing the dangerous by the non-dangerous or the less dangerous;

(g) developing a coherent overall prevention policy which covers technology, organisation of work, working conditions, social relationships and the influence of factors relating to the working environment;

(h) giving collective protective measures priority over individual protective measures; and

(i) giving appropriate instructions to employees.

Manual handling

Introduction

Most people have experienced some form of back injury in their lives, resulting in complaints such as lumbago, back strain or muscular discomfort. It is a well-established fact that over 50 per cent of all lost time injuries are associated with manual handling operations at work. These injuries can arise from simple tasks, such as moving boxes of photocopy paper, to more complicated tasks, such as lifting a patient from a wheelchair into bed in a hospital or nursing home.

It is essential, therefore, that all persons at work receive manual handling training and no one should be expected to handle loads beyond their physical capability. In particular, attention should be paid to the risks to pregnant workers and young persons arising from manual handling operations.

Principles of safe manual handling

Injuries associated with manual handling operations include prolapsed intervertebral (slipped) discs, hernias, ligamental strains and various forms of physical injury. The majority of injuries occur when actually lifting the load, so time should be taken to check the following:

1. Are there rotating or moving parts?
2. Is the load too big to handle?
3. Is the load too heavy?

Protective clothing

The following should be considered:

Hand protection

The load should be examined for evidence of sharp edges, protruding wires, splinters, etc., and suitable gloves worn if necessary.

Section A - Preliminary

*Circle as appropriate

Job descrription: Factors beyond the limits of the guidelines?	Is an assessment needed? (ie is there a potential risk for injury, and are the factors beyond the limits of the guidelines?) Yes/No*

If 'Yes' continue. If 'No' the assessment need go no further.

Operations covered by this assessment (detailed description): Locations: Personnel involved: Date of assessment:	Diagrams (other information):

Section B - See over for detailed analysis

Section C - Overall assessment of the risk of injury?   Low/ Med/ High*

Section D - Remedial action to be taken:

Remedial steps that should be taken, in order of priority: 1 2 3 4 5 6 7 8
Date by which action should be taken:
Date for reassessment:
Assessor's name: Signature:

TAKE ACTION...AND CHECK THAT IT HAS THE DESIRED EFFECT

Figure 10 Manual Handling of Loads: Assessment checklist (Source: HSE (1998) *Manual Handling,* HMSO, London.)

Section B - More detailed assessment, where necessary:

Questions to consider:	If yes, tick appropriate level of risk			Problems occurring from the task (Make rough notes in this column in preparation for the possible remedial action to be taken)	Possible remedial action (Possible changes to be made to system/task, load, workplace/space, environment. Communication that is needed)
	Low	Med	High		
The tasks – do they involve: • holding loads away from trunk? • twisting? • stooping? • reaching upwards? • large vertical movement? • long carrying distances? • strenuous pushing or pulling? • unpredictable movement of loads? • repetitive handling? • insufficient rest or recovery? • a work rate imposed by a process?					
The loads – are they: • heavy? • bulky/unwieldy? • difficult to grasp? • unstable/unpredictable? • intrinsically harmful (eg sharp/hot)?					
The working environment – are there: • constraints on posture? • poor floors? • variations in levels? • hot/cold/humid conditions? • strong air movements? • poor lighting conditions?					
Individual capability – does the job: • require unusual capability? • hazard those with a health problem? • hazard those who are pregnant? • call for special information/training?					
Other factors: Is movement or posture hindered by clothing or personal protective equipment?	Yes/No				

115

Foot protection

Footwear should be suitable for the job:

1. steel toe caps protect the feet against falling objects or if the feet could get trapped under the load;
2. steel insoles protect against protruding nails;
3. soles should be heat, oil- and acid-resistant.

Manual Handling Operations Regulations 1992 (MHOR)

Under these Regulations, each employer shall, so far as is reasonably practicable, avoid the need for any employee to undertake any manual handling operations at work which involve a risk of being injured. However, where it is not reasonably practicable to avoid this, the employer must make suitable and sufficient assessment of all such manual handling operations, and then take appropriate remedial action (see Figures 10 (pp. 114–15) and 11 (opposite)).

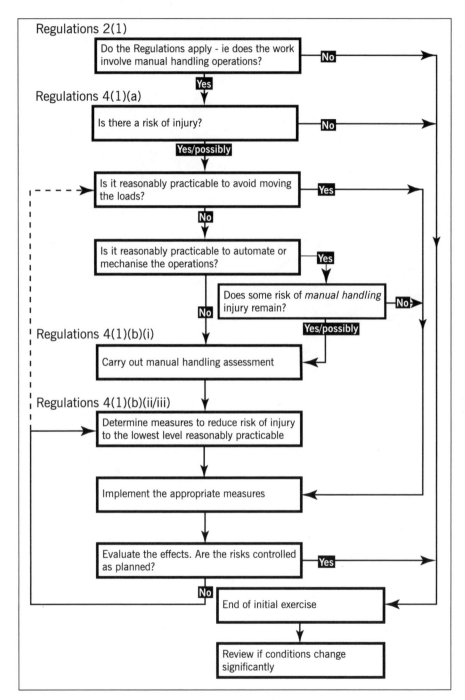

Figure 11 How to follow the Manual Handling Operations Regulations 1992 (Source: HSE (1998) *Manual Handling*, HMSO, London.)

Monitoring systems

Introduction

Systems for monitoring health and safety performance are a principal feature of the safety management process and are the starting point for all safety systems. Safety monitoring is, therefore, a proactive strategy aimed at preventing accidents and ill-health as opposed to certain reactive strategies, such as accident investigation, which are concerned with identifying where the system failed and with a view to preventing a recurrence of that accident.

In certain cases, safety monitoring activities, such as the undertaking of safety inspections or audits, may identify hazards which pose significant risks to employees and others. These significant risks may need assessing in accordance with the duties of employers under the Management of Health and Safety at Work Regulations 1999 or, in the case of substances hazardous to health, the Control of Substances Hazardous to Health (COSHH) Regulations 1999.

The various forms of safety monitoring

Health and safety performance should be monitored through one or more of the following:

Safety audits

A safety audit subjects each area of an organisation's activities to a systematic examination, with the principal objective of minimising loss. It is a continuous process aimed at ensuring effective health and safety management.

Safety audits are generally carried out using a pre-designed audit checklist to ensure a consistent approach. A specimen safety audit document is shown in Figure 12, pp. 122–7.

Safety surveys

A safety survey is a detailed examination of a number of critical areas of operation (e.g. transport safety, machinery safety or an in-depth study of the whole health and safety operation of a particular location or premises). The survey considers management and administration procedures, environmental factors, occupational health and hygiene arrangements, the broad field of safety and accident prevention and arrangements for health and safety training. It is standard practice, once the survey has been completed, for management to be presented with a phased programme of health and safety improvement covering a five-year period.

Safety inspections

This is the most commonly used form of safety monitoring and is a scheduled inspection of premises or part of the premises by various personnel (managers, safety specialists, trade union safety representatives or members of a safety committee).

Safety tours

These are an unscheduled examination of a work area, carried out by a manager, possibly accompanied by safety committee members.

Safety sampling

This technique is designed to measure, by random sampling, the accident potential in a specific workplace or at a particular process by identifying safety defects or omissions. Safety sampling entails the use of a safety sampling sheet with a limited number of aspects to be observed (machinery guards in position, ear protection being worn, housekeeping being maintained). Each of the items is graded and a maximum number of points are given for each aspect. (See Figure 13, p. 128.)

Performance monitoring and review

Monitoring encompasses the continuing assessment of the performance of the organisation, of the tasks that people undertake, and of managers and operators on an individual basis, against agreed objectives and standards. Performance monitoring is a common feature of most organisations. It implies a clear identification of the organisation's objectives, perhaps through a written 'mission statement' and the setting of policies and objectives which are both measurable and achievable by all parts of the organisation, supported by adequate resources.

At the organisational level, senior management should be aware of the various strengths and weaknesses in health and safety performance. These may be identified through various forms of active safety monitoring and through reactive monitoring systems, such as accident investigation and the analysis of accident and sickness absence returns. At the task level, the implementation of formally established safe systems of work, permit to work systems, codes of practice and operating instructions are important indicators of performance. Reactive monitoring through feedback from training exercises, in particular those aimed at increasing people's awareness, in improving attitudes to safe working and generally raising levels of knowledge of hazards, will indicate whether there has been an improvement in performance or not.

Safety performance should be related to the reward structure of the organisation in order to produce the right motivation at all levels of management.

On-the-job performance monitoring should take into account the human decision-making components of a job, in particular the potential for human error.

The Management of Health and Safety at Work Regulations 1999 (MHSWR) place an absolute duty on employers to take into account the capabilities of employees when entrusting them with tasks. Here there is a need to consider not only physical capability, for instance, to load and unload products in and out of vehicles, but also mental ability, in terms of the degree of understanding necessary for certain tasks. The latter may be achieved through the various stages of training which are aimed at ensuring competence for tasks and in continuing assessment of operators by line management.

Competent persons

Broadly, a competent person should have practical and theoretical knowledge as well as sufficient experience of the particular machinery, plant or procedure involved to enable him or her to identify defects or weaknesses during plant and machinery examinations, and to assess their importance in relation to the strength and function of that plant and machinery (*Brazier* v *Skipton Rock Company Ltd* (1962) 1 AER 955).

However, 'competent persons' are not defined in law, except in the Electricity at Work Regulations 1989 and the Pressure Systems and Transportable Gas Containers Regulations 1989. Therefore, the onus is on the employer to decide whether persons are competent to undertake these duties.

The MHSWR require an employer to appoint one or more competent persons to assist in undertaking the measures needed to comply with the requirements and prohibitions imposed by or under the relevant statutory provisions (Reg. 6(1)). One way of ensuring the operation of a safe system of work is by the designation and employment of specifically trained employees or external consultants who appreciate the risks involved.

See also COMPETENT PERSONS.

Figure 12 Specimen safety audit

Documentation	YES/NO
1. Are management aware of all health and safety legislation applying to their workplace? Is this legislation available to management and employees? 2. Have all Approved Codes of Practice, HSE Guidance Notes and internal codes of practice been studied by management with a view to ensuring compliance? 3. Does the existing Statement of Health and Safety Policy meet current conditions in the workplace? Is there a named manager with overall responsibility for health and safety? Are the organisation and arrangements' to implement the Health and Safety Policy still adequate? Have the hazards and precautions necessary on the part of staff and other persons been identified and recorded? Have individual responsibilities for health and safety been clearly detailed in the Statement? 4. Do all job descriptions adequately describe individual health and safety responsibilities and accountabilities? 5. Do written safe systems of work exist for all potentially hazardous operations? Is Permit to Work documentation available? 6. Has a suitable and sufficient assessment of the risks to staff and other persons been made, recorded and brought to the attention of staff and other persons? Have other risk assessments in respect of: (a) substances hazardous to health; (b) risks to hearing; (c) work equipment; (d) personal protective equipment; and (e) manual handling operations, been made, recorded and brought to the attention of staff and other persons? 7. Is the fire certificate available and up-to-date? Is there a record of inspections of the means of escape in the event of fire, fire appliances, fire alarms, warning notices, fire and smoke detection equipment?	

YES/NO

8. Is there a record of inspections and maintenance of work equipment, including guards and safety devices? Are all examination and test certificates available, e.g. lifting appliances and pressure sytems?
9. Are all necessary licences available, e.g. to store petroleum spirit?
10. Are workplace health and safety rules and procedures available, promoted and enforced? Have these rules and procedures been documented in a way that is comprehensible to staff and others, e.g. Health and Safety Handbook? Are disciplinary procedures for unsafe behaviour clearly documented and known to staff and other persons?
11. Is a formally written emergency procedure available?
12. Is documentation available for the recording of injuries, near misses, damage-only accidents, diseases and dangerous occurrences?
13. Are health and safety training records maintained?
14. Are there documented procedures for regulating the activities of contractors, visitors and other persons working on the site?
15. Is hazard reporting documentation available to staff and other persons?
16. Is there a documented planned maintenance system?
17. Are there written cleaning schedules?

Health and safety systems

1. Have competent persons been appointed to:
   (a) coordinate health and safety measures; and
   (b) implement the emergency procedure?
   Have these persons been adequately trained on the basis of identified and assessed risks?
   Are the role, function, responsibility and accountability of competent persons clearly identified?
2. Are there arrangements for specific forms of safety monitoring, e.g. safety inspections, safety sampling? Is a system in operation for measuring and monitoring individual management performance on health and safety issues?

3. Are systems established for the formal investigation of accidents, ill-health, near misses and dangerous occurrences? Do investigation procedures produce results which can be used to prevent future incidents? Are the causes of accidents, ill-health, near misses and dangerous occurrences analysed in terms of failure of established safe systems of work?
4. Is a hazard reporting system in operation?
5. Is a system for controlling damage to structural items, machinery, vehicles, etc. in operation?
6. Is the system for joint consultation with trade union safety representatives and staff effective? Are the role, constitution and objectives of the Health and Safety Committee clearly identified? Are the procedures for appointing or electing Committee members and trade union safety representatives clearly identified? Are the available facilities, including training arrangements, known to committee members and trade union safety representatives?
7. Are the capabilities of employees as regards health and safety taken into account when entrusting them with tasks?
8. Is the provision of first aid arrangements adequate? Are first aid personnel adequately trained and retrained?
9. Are the procedures covering sickness absence known to staff? Is there a procedure for controlling sickness absence? Are managers aware of the current sickness absence rate?
10. Do current arrangements ensure that health and safety implications are considered at the design stage of projects?
11. Is there a formally established annual health and safety budget?

Prevention and control procedures

1. Are formal inspections of machinery, plant, hand tools, access equipment, electrical equipment, storage equipment, warning systems, first aid boxes,

resuscitation equipment, welfare amenity areas, etc. undertaken? Are machinery guards and safety devices examined on a regular basis?

2. Is a Permit to Work system operated where there is a high degree of foreseeable risk?

3. Are fire and emergency procedures practised on a regular basis? Where specific fire hazards have been identified, are they catered for in the current fire protection arrangements? Are all items of fire protection equipment and alarms tested, examined and maintained on a regular basis? Are all fire exits and escape routes marked, kept free from obstruction and operational? Are all fire appliances correctly labelled, sited and maintained?

4. Is a planned maintenance system in operation?

5. Are the requirements of cleaning schedules monitored? Is housekeeping of a high standard, e.g. material storage, waste disposal, removal of spillages? Are all gangways, stairways, fire exits, access and egress points to the workplace maintained and kept clear?

6. Is environmental monitoring of temperature, lighting, ventilation, humidity, radiation, noise and vibration undertaken on a regular basis?

7. Is health surveillance of persons exposed to assessed health risks undertaken on a regular basis?

8. Is monitoring of personal exposure to assessed health risks undertaken on a regular basis?

9. Are local exhaust ventilation systems examined, tested and maintained on a regular basis?

10. Are arrangements for the storage and handling of substances hazardous to health adequate? Are all substances hazardous to health identified and correctly labelled, including transfer containers?

11. Is the appropriate personal protective equipment available? Do staff consistently wear or use the personal protective equipment when they are exposed to risks? Are storage facilities for items of personal protective equipment provided?

12. Are welfare amenity provisions, i.e. sanitation, hand

washing, showers and clothing storage arrangements, adequate? Do welfare amenity provisions promote appropriate levels of personal hygiene?

Information, instruction, training and supervision

1. Is the information provided by manufacturers and suppliers of articles and substances for use at work adequate? Do employees and other persons have access to this information?
2. Is the means of promoting health and safety adequate? Is effective use made of safety propaganda, e.g. posters?
3. Do current safety signs meet the requirements of the Safety Signs Regulations 1980 and the Health and Safety (Safety Signs and Signals) Regulations 1996? Are safety signs adequate in terms of the assessed risks?
4. Are fire instructions prominently displayed?
5. Are hazard warning systems adequate?
6. Are the individual training needs of staff and other persons assessed on a regular basis?
7. Is staff health and safety training undertaken:
    (a) at the induction stage;
    (b) on their being exposed to new or increased risks because of:
        (i)   transfer or change in responsibilities;
        (ii) the introduction of new work equipment or a change respecting existing work equipment:
        (iii) the introduction of new technology;
        (iv) the introduction of a new system of work or change in an existing system of work.
    Is the above training:
    (a) repeated periodically;
    (b) adapted to take account of new or changed risks; and
    (c) carried out during working hours?
8. Is specific training carried out regularly for first aid

YES/NO

staff, forklift truck drivers, crane drivers and others exposed to specific risks? Are selected staff trained in the correct use of fire appliances?

Final question

Are you satisfied that your organisation is as safe and healthy as you can reasonably make it, or that you know what action must be taken to achieve that state?

Action plan

1. Immediate action

2. Short-term action (fourteen days)

3. Medium-term action (six months)

4. Long-term action (two years)

_____   _____

Auditor   Date
_____

		Area A	Area B	Area C
1.	Housekeeping/cleaning (max. 10)			
2.	Personal protection (max. 10)			
3.	Machinery safety (max. 10)			
4.	Chemical storage (max. 5)			
5.	Chemical handling (max. 5)			
6.	Manual handling (max. 5)			
7.	Fire protection (max. 10)			
8.	Structural safety (max. 10)			
9.	Internal transport (max. 5)			
10.	Access equipment (max. 5)			
11.	First aid provision (max. 5)			
12.	Hand tools (max. 10)			
13.	Internal storage (racking) (max. 5)			
14.	Electrical safety (max. 10)			
15.	Temperature control (max. 5)			
16.	Lighting (max. 5)			
17.	Ventilation (max. 5)			
18.	Noise control (max. 5)			
19.	Dust and fume control (max. 5)			
20.	Welfare amenity provisions (max. 10)			
	TOTAL (max. 140)			

Figure 13 Safety sampling exercise

Noise at work

Introduction

'Noise' is generally defined as 'unwanted sound'. Noise can be a nuisance both at common law and under statute law due to individual disturbance and loss of enjoyment of life, loss of sleep and fatigue that it can create.

Second, it can distract attention and concentration, mask audible warning signals or interfere with work, thereby becoming a causative factor in accidents. Finally, exposure to excessive noise can result in hearing impairment, the condition known as 'noise-induced hearing loss' or 'occupational deafness'.

The effects of exposure

Exposure to noise may affect hearing in three ways:

1. *Temporary threshold shift* is the short-term effect, that is, a temporary reduction in hearing acuity, which may follow exposure to noise. The condition is reversible and the effect depends to some extent on individual susceptibility.
2. *Permanent threshold shift* takes place when the limit of tolerance is exceeded in terms of time, the level of noise and individual susceptibility. Recovery from permanent threshold shift will not proceed to completion, but will effectively cease at some particular point in time after the end of the exposure.
3. *Acoustic trauma* is a quite different condition from occupational deafness (noise-induced hearing loss). It involves sudden aural damage resulting from short-term intense exposure or even from one single exposure. Explosive pressure rises are often responsible, such as that resulting from gunfire, major explosions or even fireworks.

Noise dose

For most steady types of industrial noise, intensity and duration of exposure (dose) are the principal factors in the degree of noise-induced hearing loss. Furthermore, hearing ability deteriorates with age (presbycusis), and it is sometimes difficult to distinguish between the effects of noise and normal age deterioration in hearing. Research by the UK Medical Research Council and the National Physical Laboratory has shown that the risk of noise-induced hearing loss can be related to the total amount of noise energy that is taken in by the ears over a working lifetime.

The symptoms of occupational deafness

Symptoms of noise-induced hearing loss vary according to whether the hearing loss is mild or severe. Typical symptoms associated with a mild form of hearing loss include difficulties in conversation with people, the wrong answers may be given occasionally due to the individual missing certain key elements of the question, and speech on television and radio seems indistinct. There may be difficulty in hearing normal domestic sounds, such as a clock ticking.

With a severe degree of deafness there is difficulty in discussion, even when face-to-face with people, as well as hearing what is said at public meetings, unless sitting right at the front. Generally, people seem to be speaking indistinctly, even on radio and television, and there is an inability to hear the normal sounds of the home and street. It is often impossible to tell the direction from which a source of noise is coming, and to assess the distance from the sound. In the most severe cases, there is a sensation of whistling or ringing in the ears (tinnitus).

Noise control

In any strategy to reduce or control noise two factors must be considered, that is, the actual source of the noise and, second, the transmission pathway taken by the noise to the recipient. Personal protective equipment, such as ear plugs, ear defenders and acoustic wool, may go some way towards preventing people from going deaf at work, but such a strategy must be regarded as a secondary form of protection since it relies too heavily upon exposed persons wearing potentially uncomfortable and inconvenient protection for all the time they are exposed to noise.

The design stage

The first consideration must be that of tackling a potential noise problem at the design stage of new projects, rather than endeavouring to control noise once the machinery or noise-emitting item of plant is installed.

Manufacturers and suppliers of machinery and plant must be required to give an indication of anticipated sound pressure levels emitted by their equipment and of the measures necessary, in certain cases, to reduce such noise emission, prior to the ordering of same.

Existing machinery and plant

In the case of existing machinery and plant, different methods of noise control are suitable for dealing with different sources and for the possible stages in the transmission pathway. These may be summarised in the Table 4. Control of the main or primary pathway is the most important factor in noise control and in ensuring compliance with the Noise at Work Regulations.

Table 4 Methods of noise control

Sources and pathways	Control measures
Vibration produced through machinery operation	Reduction at source, e.g. substitution with nylon components for metal; use of tapered tools on power presses
Structure-borne noise (vibration)	Vibration isolation, e.g. use of resilient mounts and connections, anti-vibration mounts
Radiation of structural vibration	Vibration damping to prevent resonance
Turbulence created by air or gas flow	Reduction at source or the use of silencers
Airborne noise pathway	Noise insulation reflection; use of heavy barriers
	Noise absorption no reflection; use of porous lightweight barriers

Occupational health and hygiene

Introduction

Every year people at work contract various forms of occupational disease or condition, some of which prove fatal (e.g. occupational cancer, pneumoconiosis or chemical poisoning). Other people may become permanently incapacitated through conditions such as noise-induced hearing loss (occupational deafness) or vibration-induced injury. Occupational dermatitis is the most common form of occupational disease.

Occupational health is a branch of preventative medicine concerned with the relationship between work and health and the effects of work on the worker.

Occupational hygiene involves the identification, measurement, evaluation and control of contaminants and other phenomena, such as noise and radiation, which could have unacceptable adverse effects on the health of people exposed to them.Occupational hygiene practice is principally concerned with the prevention or control of a wide range of environmental stressors, such as bacteria, gases, fumes, fogs, mists and dusts. It is also concerned with the measurement, evaluation and control of the stressor, e.g. noise and vibration.

Stages of occupational hygiene practice

Occupational hygiene practice takes a number of clearly identified stages:

1. identification of the stressor (e.g. noise, dust, gases);
2. measurement of the extent of the stressor, using prescribed sampling techniques;
3. evaluation of the risks by reference to established criteria, such as Occupational Exposure Limits published by the Health and Safety Executive (HSE);
4. selection of a prevention or control strategy, such as the installation of a local exhaust ventilation system to remove dust from a process;
5. implementation of that strategy;

6. monitoring of the working environment to ensure the prevention or control strategy installed is effective.

Environmental stressors

The various forms of environmental stressor can be classified as follows:

Physical

The effects of exposure to extremes of temperature and humidity, inadequate lighting and ventilation, noise and vibration, radiation.

Chemical

The effects of exposure to toxic, corrosive, harmful or irritant solids, liquids and gases.

Biological

The effects of exposure to bacteria, viruses, zoonoses, etc.

Ergonomic/work-related

The effects on people of poorly designed working layouts and workstations, which can lead to various forms of fatigue and physical and/or mental stress.

Strategy factors

Any strategy designed to prevent or reduce the risk of people contracting various forms of ill-health at work should take the following factors into account:

1. measures to prevent or reduce the risk of occupational disease;
2. systems for the identification, measurement, evaluation and control of occupational health risks in the working environment;
3. the arrangements for welfare amenities;
4. FIRST AID and emergency services;
5. the ergonomic aspects of jobs;
6. the selection, provision, suitability, maintenance and use of PERSONAL PROTECTIVE EQUIPMENT (PPE).

Practitioners in occupational health and hygiene

Various specialists are involved in the practice of occupational health and hygiene. These include occupational physicians, occupational hygienists, occupational health nurses and health and safety practitioners. Each of these groups has a specific contribution to make in preventing ill-health arising from workplace operations and activities.

Principal areas of occupational health practice

Placing people in suitable work

The aim is to assess current mental and physical capability and to identify pre-existing ill-health conditions.

Health surveillance

This entails specific health examinations at a predetermined frequency for:

1. those at risk of developing further ill-health or disability, e.g. people exposed to excessive noise levels; and
2. those actually or potentially at risk by virtue of the type of work they undertake during their employment, e.g. radiation workers.

Providing a treatment service

The efficient and speedy treatment of injuries, acute poisonings and minor ailments at work is a standard feature of occupational health practice.

Primary and secondary monitoring

Primary monitoring is largely concerned with the clinical observation of people who seek treatment or advice on their condition. Secondary monitoring is directed at controlling the hazards to health which have already been recognised, e.g. audiometry.

Avoiding potential risks

Here the principal emphasis is on prevention, in preference to treatment, for a known condition.

Supervision of vulnerable groups

Vulnerable workers include young persons, pregnant women, the aged, the disabled and people who may have long periods of sickness absence. Routine health examinations to assess continuing fitness for work may be incorporated.

Monitoring for early evidence of non-occupational disease

This entails the routine monitoring of workers not exposed to health risks with the principal objective controlling diseases prevalent in certain communities (e.g. mining), with a view to their eventual eradication.

Counselling

Counselling on health-related issues and on personal, social and emotional problems is a standard area of occupational health practice.

Health education

This is primarily concerned with the education of employees towards a healthier lifestyle. It can also include training of management and staff in their respective responsibilities for health and safety at work, in healthy working techniques and in the avoidance of health risks.

First aid and emergency services

This area may include the supervision of first aid arrangements, training of first aid staff and the preparation of contingency arrangements in the event of fire, explosion or other emergencies.

Environmental control and occupational hygiene

This entails the identification, measurement, evaluation and control of potential health risks to employees and the general public from processes and premises, together with the prevention and control of environmental nuisances.

Liaison

Occupational health staff liaise with enforcement agency staff, such as employment medical advisers and employment nursing advisers, and other public agencies.

Health records

The completion and maintenance of health records is required under certain Regulations and for internal purposes to ensure continuing surveillance procedures are maintained.

Occupational diseases and conditions

It is important to distinguish between the terms reportable diseases and prescribed diseases.

Reportable diseases

These are diseases which are reportable to the enforcing authority (HSE or local authority) in accordance with the requirements of the Reporting of Injuries, Diseases and Dangerous Occurrences Regulations 1995 (RIDDOR).

Prescribed diseases

Prescribed diseases are covered by the Social Security (Industrial Injuries) (Prescribed Diseases) Regulations 1985. A disease may be prescribed for the purposes of industrial injuries benefit if:

1. it ought to be treated, having regard to its causes and incidence and other relevant considerations, as a risk of occupation and not a risk common to all persons; and
2. it is such that, in the absence of special circumstances, the attribution of particular cases to the nature of the employment can be established with reasonable certainty.

Classification of causes of occupational disease

These are classified into the following four categories:

Physical causes

- *Heat* – heat cataract, heat stroke (prescribed disease A2).
- *Lighting* – miner's nystagmus (prescribed disease A9).
- *Noise* – noise-induced hearing loss (occupational deafness) (prescribed disease A10).
- *Vibration* – vibration-induced white finger (VWF) (prescribed disease All).
- *Radiation* – radiation sickness (at ionising wavelengths), burns, arc eye.
- *Dust* – silicosis, coal worker's pneumoconiosis (prescribed disease D1).
- *Pressure* – decompression sickness (prescribed disease A3).

Chemical causes

- *Acids and alkalis* – dermatitis (non-infective dermatitis) (prescribed disease D5).
- *Metals* – lead and mercury poisoning (prescribed diseases C1 and C5, respectively).
- *Non-metals* – arsenic and phosphorus poisoning (prescribed diseases C4 and C3, respectively).
- *Gases* – carbon monoxide poisoning, arsine poisoning (prescribed disease C4).

- *Organic compounds* – occupational cancers, e.g. bladder cancer (prescribed disease C23).
- *Chemical dusts* – mercury poisoning (prescribed disease C5).

Biological causes

- *Animal-borne diseases* (zoonoses) – anthrax, brucellosis, glanders fever (prescribed diseases B1, B2 and B7, respectively).
- *Human-borne* – viral hepatitis (prescribed disease B8).
- *Vegetable-borne* – aspergillosis (farmer's lung) (prescribed disease B6).

Ergonomic (work-related) causes

- *Job movements* – cramp, relation to handwriting or typewriting (prescribed disease A4).
- *Friction and pressure* – bursitis, cellulitis, 'beat conditions', e.g. traumatic inflammation of the tendons or associated tendon sheaths of the hand or forearm (prescribed diseases AS and A8).

Social Security (Industrial Injuries) (Prescribed Diseases) Regulations 1985

These Regulations (amended in 1987 and 1989) list those diseases prescribed for the purpose of payment of disablement benefit. A prescribed disease is defined in the Social Security Act 1975 as:

1. a disease which ought to be treated, having regard to its causes and incidence and other relevant considerations, as a risk of occupation and not a risk common to all persons; and
2. it is such that, in the absence of special circumstances, the attribution of particular cases to the nature of the employment can be established with reasonable certainty.

Schedule 1 to the Regulations classifies prescribed diseases or injuries thus:

1. conditions due to physical agents;
2. conditions due to biological agents;
3. conditions due to chemical agents; and
4. miscellaneous conditions.

Within these four classifications, prescribed diseases or injuries are related to specific occupations. Each disease is numbered within the particular classification.

Occupiers' liability

Introduction

People who occupy land and premises, such as householders, local authorities, companies, organisations, shopkeepers and operators of licensed premises, have a range of liabilities. Their land and premises are visited by people for a variety of purposes, for instance, to carry out work, provide goods and services, settle accounts, etc. The Health and Safety at Work Act requires those people in control of premises to take reasonable care towards these other persons, and failure to comply with this duty can lead to prosecution and a fine on conviction.

Furthermore, anyone who is injured while visiting or working on land or premises may be in a position to sue the occupier for damages, even though the injured person may not be their employee. Lord Gardner in the case of *Commissioner for Railways v McDermott* [1967] 1 AC 169 explained the position thus:

> *Occupation of premises is a ground of liability and is not a ground of exemption from liability. It is a ground of liability because it gives some control over and knowledge of the state of the premises, and it is natural and right that the occupier should have some degree of responsibility for the safety of persons entering his premises with his permission ... there is 'proximity between the occupier and such persons and they are his 'neighbours'. Thus arises a duty of care ...*

Occupier's liability is, therefore, a branch of the civil law concerned with the duties of occupiers of premises to all those who may enter on to those premises. The legislation covering this area of civil liability is the Occupiers Liability Act (OLA) 1957 and, specifically in the case of trespassers, the Occupiers Liability Act 1984.

Occupiers' Liability Act 1957

Under the Act an occupier owes a common duty of care to all lawful visitors. This common duty of care is defined as:

> *a duty to take such care as in all the circumstances of the case is reasonable to*

see that the visitor will be reasonably safe in using the premises for the purposes for which he is invited or permitted by the occupier to be there.

The Act defines the duty owed by occupiers of premises to all persons lawfully on the premises in respect of dangers due to the state of the premises or to things done or omitted to be done on them.

The Act further regulates the nature of the duty imposed in consequence of a person's occupation of premises. The duties are not personal duties but rather, are based on the occupation of premises, and extend to a person occupying, or having control over, any fixed or movable structure, including any vessel, vehicle or aircraft.

Visitors

Protection is afforded to all lawful visitors, whether they enter for the occupier's benefit, such as customers or clients, or for their own benefit, for instance, a police officer, though not to persons exercising a public or private right of way over premises.

Warning Notices

Occupiers have a duty to erect notices warning visitors of imminent danger, such as an uncovered pit or obstruction. However a warning notice does not, in itself, absolve the occupier from liability, unless, in all the circumstances, it was sufficient to enable the visitor to be reasonably safe.

Furthermore, while an occupier, under the provisions of the Act, could have excused his liability by displaying a suitable prominent and carefully worded notice, the chance of such avoidance is not permitted as a result of the Unfair Contract Terms Act 1977. This Act states that it is not permissible to exclude liability for death or injury due to negligence by a contract or by a notice, including a notice displayed in accordance with the OLA.

The Occupiers' Liability Act 1984 – Trespassers

A trespasser is defined in common law as a person who:

1. goes on premises without invitation or permission;
2. although invited or permitted to be on premises, goes to a part of the premises to which the invitation or permission does not extend;
3. remains on premises after the invitation or permission to be there has expired;
4. deposits goods on premises when not authorised to do so.

The OLA 1984 imposes a duty on an occupier in respect of trespassers, namely persons who may have a lawful authority to be in the vicinity or not, who may be at risk of injury on the occupier's premises.

This duty can be discharged by issuing some form of warning such as the display of hazard warning notices, but such warnings must be very explicit. For example, it is insufficient to display a notice that states merely:

> **DANGEROUS**
> **BULL**

where there may be a risk to visitors from a potentially dangerous bull whilst crossing the field where the bull is kept.

A suitable notice in such circumstances might read:

> **DANGEROUS BULL**
> **USE THE DESIGNATED FOOTPATH**

Furthermore, it is not sufficient merely to display a notice. In this case the requirements of the notice must be actively enforced by the occupier of the land.

Generally, the displaying of a notice, the clarity, legibility and explicitness of such a notice, and evidence of regularly reminding people of the message outlined in the notice, may count to a certain extent as part of a defence when sued for injury by a simple trespasser under the Act.

Children

Children, from a legal viewpoint, have always been deemed to be less responsible than adults. The OLA 1957 is quite specific on this matter.

Broadly, an occupier must be prepared for children to be less careful than adults. Where, for instance, there is something, or a situation, on the premises that is a lure or attraction to a child, such as a pond, an old motor car, a derelict building or scaffolding surrounding a building, this can constitute a 'trap' as far as a child is concerned. Should a child be injured as a result of this trap, the occupier could then be liable.

Contractors

The relationship between occupiers and contractors has been the subject of much controversy. The OLA 1957 states that 'an occupier may expect that a person, in exercising his calling, such as a window cleaner, bricklayer or painter, will appreciate and guard against any risks ordinarily incident to that calling, for instance the risk of falling, so far as the occupier gives them leave to do so'. This means that the risks associated with the system of work on third party premises are the responsibility of the contractor's employer, not the occupier.

> **Note**
>
> It should be appreciated that while the above may be the case at civil law, the situation at criminal law, namely the duties owed by employers to non-employees under section 3 of the HSWA, is different.

Where a contractors are working on a premises, the occupier may not be not liable if he:

1. took care to select a competent contractor; and
2. satisfied himself that the work was being properly done by the contractor.

This relationship between occupiers and contractors has been substantially modified and extended through the Construction (Design and Management) Regulations 1994. (See also CONTRACTORS.)

Personal protective equipment

Introduction

The provision and use of some form of personal protective equipment (PPE), such as a respirator, safety helmet or gloves, is a very common 'safe person' strategy. Moreover, it is seen by many employers as a quick and easy solution to dealing with hazards at work, relieving them of taking more effective measures to prevent exposure to hazards.

However, it is not a perfect solution and never will be, as it relies heavily on the employee wearing the PPE all the time that he is exposed to the hazard and, most importantly, wearing it correctly. In many cases, employees simply will not do this, complaining, for example, that the PPE is uncomfortable, hinders the execution of the task effectively or obscures vision.

On this basis, the use of PPE must be seen as the last resort, when all other protection methods have failed, or, perhaps, as an interim measure until some form of 'safe place' strategy, such as the installation of local exhaust ventilation in dusty processes, can be implemented.

Definition

Under the Personal Protective Equipment at Work Regulations 1992 (PPEWR), PPE is defined as 'all equipment (including clothing affording protection against the weather) which is intended to be worn or held by a person at work and which protects him against one or more risks to his health or safety, and any addition or accessory designed to meet that objective'.

Forms of PPE

A wide range of PPE is available.

Head protection

Industrial safety helmets, various forms of riding helmets, industrial scalp protectors (bump caps), caps and hairnets.

Eye protection

Safety spectacles, eye shields, safety goggles and face shields.

Face protection

Face shields, hand-held, fixed to a helmet or strapped to the head.

Respiratory protection

General-purpose dust respirators, positive pressure-powered dust respirators, helmet-contained positive pressure respirators, gas respirators, emergency escape respirators, air-line breathing apparatus, self-contained breathing apparatus.

Hearing protection

Ear plugs, ear defenders, muffs and pads, ear valves, acoustic wool.

Skin protection

Barrier creams and sprays.

Body protection

One- and two-piece overalls, donkey jackets, rubber and PVC-coated aprons, vapour suits, splash-resistant suits, warehouse coats, body warmers, thermal and weather protection overclothing, oilskin overclothing, high visibility clothing, personal buoyancy equipment, such as life-jackets.

Hand and arm protection

General-purpose fibre gloves, PVC fabric gauntlets, leather gloves and sleeves, wrist protectors, chain mail hand and arm protectors.

Leg and foot protection

Safety boots and shoes, wellington boots, clogs, foundry boots, anti-static footwear, gaiters and anklets.

Limitations in the use of PPE

Personal protective equipment should be seen either as an interim measure or as the last resort, when all other protection strategies have failed. But simply providing PPE is never the solution because employees often fail to use it. Its selection, therefore, is critical.

Selection of PPE

The PPEWR place a duty on employers to ensure that any PPE provided is 'suitable' (Reg. 4). When considering the type and form of equipment to be provided, and its relative suitability, the following factors are relevant:

1. the needs of the user in terms of comfort, ease of movement, convenience in putting on, use and removal, and individual suitability;
2. the ergonomic requirements and state of health of the persons who may use it;
3. correct fit, after adjustments within the range for which it is designed;
4. the number of personnel exposed to a particular hazard;
5. the risk or risks involved and the conditions at the site;
6. its relative effectiveness to prevent or adequately control the risk or risks without increasing overall risk;
7. the scale of the hazard;
8. standards representing recognised 'safe limits' for the hazard, e.g. detailed in Health and Safety Executive (HSE) Guidance Notes, British Standards;
9. specific Regulations currently in force, e.g. Noise at Work Regulations 1989, Control of Substances Hazardous to Health Regulations 1999 (COSHHR);
10. specific job requirements or restrictions, e.g. work in confined spaces, roof work;
11. the presence of environmental stressors;
12. the ease of cleaning, sanitising, maintenance and replacement of equipment and/or its component parts.

Preventive maintenance

Introduction

Under the Workplace (Health, Safety and Welfare) Regulations 1992 there is an absolute duty on employers to ensure the workplace and equipment, devices and systems shall be maintained (including cleaned as appropriate) in an efficient state, in efficient working order and in good repair. Similar duties, in respect of work equipment, are imposed on employers under the Provision and Use of Work Equipment Regulations 1998.

An important feature of health and safety management is, therefore, the operation of planned preventive maintenance programmes for the workplace, items of work equipment, systems and devices and, in some cases, for vehicles, such as lift trucks.

Planned preventive maintenance programmes

Such programmes generally involve written schedules which should incorporate the following features:

1. the workplace structure, item of work equipment, safety system, vehicle, etc., to be maintained by reference to a plant, structural or vehicle maintenance register;
2. the maintenance procedure to be followed, including specific work methods, the materials and equipment to be used and, for work equipment, the criteria for testing and examination following the maintenance operation;
3. the frequency of maintenance, e.g. at the end of each production run, daily, weekly, every 5,000 miles, etc.;
4. identification of the person with specific responsibility for ensuring the written maintenance procedure has been correctly applied; and
5. details of hazards and the specific precautions to be taken by employees carrying out maintenance work, such as the operation of a permit to work system and the use of specific personal protective equipment.

Regular monitoring to ensure correct implementation of the programme should be undertaken by a senior manager, e.g. engineering director, chief engineer, with corrective action being taken where necessary. Records of preventive maintenance undertaken should be maintained, which as well as serving commercial records, could also be of value in the event of any legal action.

Reporting and recording

Introduction

Current legislation places a duty on employers and others to notify and report injuries and diseases, together with other scheduled incidents and occurrences with the potential to cause death, injury or disease, to the enforcing authority. In certain cases, officers of the enforcing authority may decide to investigate such events to determine the causes of same and to ascertain whether there has been a breach of health and safety legislation.

Under the Reporting of Injuries, Diseases and Dangerous Occurrences Regulations 1995 (RIDDOR) a 'responsible person' must notify, by quickest practicable means (e.g. telephone or fax) and report within ten days to the enforcing authority, certain classes of injury sustained by people at work, various occupational diseases and defined dangerous occurrences as listed in the Schedule to the Regulations.

Specified major injury or condition

A major injury or condition means:

1. any fracture, other than to the fingers, thumbs or toes;
2. any amputation;
3. dislocation of the shoulder, hip, knee or spine;
4. loss of sight (whether temporary or permanent);
5. a chemical or hot metal burn to the eye or any penetrating injury to the eye;
6. any injury resulting from electric shock or electrical burn (including any electrical burn caused by arcing or arcing products) leading to unconsciousness or requiring resuscitation or admittance to hospital for more than 24 hours;
7. any other injury:
   (a) leading to hypothermia, heat-induced illness or to unconsciousness,
   (b) requiring resuscitation, or
   (c) requiring admittance to hospital for more than 24 hours;

8. loss of consciousness caused by asphyxia or by exposure to a harmful substance or biological agent;
9. either of the following conditions which result from the absorption of any substance by inhalation, ingestion or through the skin:
    (a) acute illness requiring medical treatment, or
    (b) loss of consciousness;
10. acute illness which requires medical treatment where there is reason to believe that this resulted from exposure to a biological agent or its toxins or infected material.

Reportable diseases

The responsible person must send a report to the enforcing authority on the approved form (Form 2508A; see Figure 14, pp. 151–2) wherever a person suffers from one of the reportable diseases (examples are listed in Table 5, below).

Dangerous occurrence

This is an occurrence which arises out of or in connection with work and is of a class specified in Schedule 2 of the Regulations.

Notification and reporting of injuries and dangerous occurrences

Where any person, as a result of an accident arising out of or in connection with work, dies or suffers any of the specific major injuries or conditions, or where there is a dangerous occurrence, the responsible person shall:

1. notify the enforcing authority by quickest practicable means; and
2. within ten days send a report thereof to the enforcing authority on a form approved for this purpose (Form 2508; see Figure 15, pp. 153–4).

Where a person at work is incapacitated for work of a kind which he or she

Table 5 Examples of reportable diseases

Disease	Work activity
9. Subcutaneous cellulitis	Physically demanding work causing severe or prolonged friction or pressure of the hand
25. Tetanus	Work involving contact with soil likely to be contaminated by animals
38. Skin cancer	Work involving exposure to mineral oil tar, pitch or arsenic

Health and Safety at Work etc Act 1974
The Reporting of Injuries, Diseases and Dangerous Occurrences Regulations 1995

HSE
Health & Safety
Executive

Report of a case of disease

Filling in this form
This form must be filled in by an employer or other responsible person.

Part A
About you
1 What is your full name?

2 What is your job title?

3 What is your telephone number?

About your organisation
4 What is the name of your organisation?

5 What is its address and postcode?

6 Does the affected person usually work at this address?
Yes ☐ Go to question 7
No ☐ Where do they normally work?

7 What type of work does the organisation do?

Part B
About the affected person
1 What is their full name?

2 What is their date of birth?
/ /

3 What is their job title?

4 Are they?
☐ male?
☐ female?

5 Is the affected person (tick one box)
☐ one of your employees?
☐ on a training scheme? Give details:

☐ on work experience?
☐ employed by someone else?

☐ other? Give details:

Continued overleaf

F2508A (01/96)

Figure 14 Report of a case of disease (Source: HSE)

Part C

The disease you are reporting

1 Please give:

- **the name of the disease, and the type of work it is associated with; or**

- **the name and number of the disease**

  (from Schedule 3 of the Regulations – see the accompanying notes).

2 What is the date of the statement of the doctor who first diagnosed or confirmed the disease?

```
    /     /
```

3 What is the name and address of the doctor?

Continue your description here

Part D

Describing the work that led to the disease

Please describe any work done by the affected person which might have led to them getting the disease.

If the disease is thought to have been caused by exposure to an agent at work (*eg a specific chemical*) please say what that agent is.

Give any other information which is relevant.

Give your description here

Part E

Your signature

Signature

Date

```
    /     /
```

Where to send the form

Please send it to the Enforcing Authority for the place where the affected person works. If you do not know the Enforcing Authority, send it to the nearest HSE office.

For official use

Client number

Location number

Event number

☐ INV   REP   ☐ Y   ☐ N

Health and Safety at Work etc Act 1974
The Reporting of Injuries, Diseases and Dangerous Occurrences Regulations 1995

HSE
Health & Safety
Executive

Report of an injury or dangerous occurrence

Filling in this form
This form must be filled in by an employer or other responsible person.

Part A

About you
1 What is your full name?

2 What is your job title?

3 What is your telephone number?

About your organisation
4 What is the name of your organisation?

5 What is its address and postcode?

6 What type of work does the organisation do?

Part B

About the incident
1 On what date did the incident happen?

    /   /

2 At what time did the incident happen?
(Please use the 24-hour clock eg 0600)

3 Did the incident happen at the above address?

Yes ☐ Go to question 4
No ☐ Where did the incident happen?
    ☐ elsewhere in your organisation – give the
       name, address and postcode
    ☐ at someone else's premises – give the name,
       address and postcode
    ☐ in a public place – give details of where it
       happened

If you do not know the postcode, what is
the name of the local authority?

4 In which department, or where on the premises,
did the incident happen?

Part C

About the injured person
If you are reporting a dangerous occurrence, go
to Part F.
If more than one person was injured in the same incident,
please attach the details asked for in Part C and Part D
for each injured person.

1 What is their full name?

2 What is their home address and postcode?

3 What is their home phone number?

4 How old are they?

5 Are they?
    ☐ male?
    ☐ female?

6 What is their job title?

7 Was the injured person (tick one box only)
    ☐ one of your employees?
    ☐ on a training scheme? Give details:

    ☐ on work experience?
    ☐ employed by someone else? Give details of the
       employer:

    ☐ self-employed and at work?
    ☐ a member of the public?

Part D

About the injury
1 What was the injury? (eg fracture, laceration)

2 What part of the body was injured?

Figure 15 Report of an injury or dangerous occurrence (Source: HSE)

3 Was the injury (tick one box that applies)
☐ a fatality?

☐ a major injury or condition? (see accompanying notes)

☐ an injury to an employee or self-employed person which prevented them doing their normal work for more than 3 days?

☐ an injury to a member of the public which meant they had to be taken from the scene of the accident to a hospital for treatment?

4 Did the injured person (tick all the boxes that apply)
☐ become unconscious?

☐ need resuscitation?

☐ remain in hospital for more than 24 hours?

☐ none of the above.

Part E

About the kind of accident

Please tick the one box that best describes what happened, then go to Part G.

☐ Contact with moving machinery or material being machined

☐ Hit by a moving, flying or falling object

☐ Hit by a moving vehicle

☐ Hit something fixed or stationary

☐ Injured while handling, lifting or carrying

☐ Slipped, tripped or fell on the same level

☐ Fell from a height

How high was the fall?

| metres |

☐ Trapped by something collapsing

☐ Drowned or asphyxiated

☐ Exposed to, or in contact with, a harmful substance

☐ Exposed to fire

☐ Exposed to an explosion

☐ Contact with electricity or an electrical discharge

☐ Injured by an animal

☐ Physically assaulted by a person

☐ Another kind of accident (describe it in Part G)

Part F

Dangerous occurrences

Enter the number of the dangerous occurrences you are reporting. (The numbers are given in the Regulations and in the notes which accompany this form)

Part G

Describing what happened

Give as much detail as you can. For instance
- the name of any substance involved
- the name and type of machine involved
- the event that led to the incident
- the part played by any people

If it was a personal injury, give details of what the person was doing. Describe any action that has since been taken to prevent a similar incident. Use a separate piece of paper if you need to.

Part H

Your signature

Signature

Date
| / | / |

Where to send the form
Please send it to the Enforcing Authority for the place where it happened. If you do not know the Enforcing Authority, send it to the nearest HSE office.

For official use

Client number	Location number	Event number	
			☐ INV REP ☐ Y ☐ N

might reasonably be expected to do, either under a contract of employment or in the normal course of work, for more than three consecutive days (excluding the day of the accident but including any days which would not have been working days) because of an injury (other than a specified major injury) resulting from an accident at work, the responsible person shall within ten days of the accident send a report to the enforcing authority on the form approved for this purpose (Form 2508).

Reporting the death of an employee

Where an employee, as a result of an accident at work, has suffered a specified major injury or condition which is the cause of his or her death within one year of the date of the accident, the employer shall inform the enforcing authority in writing of the death as soon as it comes to his or her knowledge, whether or not the accident had been reported previously.

Reporting a case of disease

Where a person at work suffers from a reportable disease, the responsible person shall send a report to the enforcing authority on Form 2508A. This requirement applies only if:

1. in the case of an employee or a person undergoing training, the responsible person has received a written statement prepared by a registered medical practitioner diagnosing the disease as one of the reportable diseases; or
2. in the case of a self-employed person, that person has been informed by a registered medical practitioner that he or she is suffering from the disease so specified.

Records

The responsible person shall keep a record of any event or any disease which is required to be reported under Regulation 3. The records must be kept at the workplace or, if that is not practicable, at the usual place of business of the responsible person, and must be kept for at least three years.

The responsible person shall send to the enforcing authority such extracts from the records required to be kept as the enforcing authority may from time to time require.

Accident books

Under the Social Security Act 1975:

1. Employees must notify their employer of any accident resulting in personal injury in respect of which benefit may be payable. Notification may be given by a third party if the employee is incapacitated.

2. Employees must enter the appropriate particulars of all accidents in an Accident Book (Form BI 510). This may be done by another person if the employee is incapacitated. Such an entry is deemed to satisfy the requirements in 1 above.

3. Employers must investigate all accidents of which notice is given by employees. Variations in the findings of this investigation and the particulars given in the notification must be recorded.

4. Employers must, on request, furnish the Department of Social Security with such information as may be required relating to accidents in respect of which benefit may be payable, e.g. Forms 2508 and 2508A.

5. Employers must provide and keep readily available an Accident Book in an approved form in which the appropriate details of all accidents can be recorded (Form BI 150). Such books, when completed, should be retained for three years after the date of the last entry.

Representation

Introduction

The Health and Safety at Work etc. Act 1974 places a duty on employers to consult with trade union-appointed safety representatives 'with a view to making and maintaining arrangements that will enable them and their employees to co-operate effectively in promoting and developing measures to ensure the health and safety at work of the employees, and in checking the effectiveness of such measures'. This duty was reinforced in the Safety Representatives and Safety Committees Regulations 1977.

More recent legislation, the Health and Safety (Consultation with Employees) Regulations 1996, has extended this duty on employers to consult with employees where no trade union safety representation exists.

Safety representatives

The Regulations cover the following issues in relation to safety representatives:

Appointment of safety representatives

1. The safety representative is not appointed by the safety committee (and vice versa); nor is he or she responsible to the safety committee (and vice versa).
2. A recognised trade union may appoint safety representatives from amongst the employees in all cases where one or more employees are employed by an employer by whom it is recognised.
3. The employer must be notified by the trade union of the names of the safety representatives.
4. Each safety representative is required to have certain prescribed functions.

Functions of safety representatives

Safety representatives have the following functions:

1. to represent employees in consultation with employers;
2. to cooperate effectively in promoting and developing health and safety measures;
3. to make representations to the employer on any general or specific matter affecting the health and safety of their members;
4. to make representations to the employer on general matters affecting the health and safety of other persons employed at the workplace;
5. to carry out certain inspections;
6. to represent members in consultations with the HSE;
7. to receive information from Inspectors;
8. to attend meetings of the safety committee if appropriate.

None of these functions imposes a duty on safety representatives.

Time off with pay

Employers must give safety representatives time off with pay for performing their functions and for any reasonable training they may undergo.

Inspections of the workplace

Safety representatives are entitled to carry out workplace inspections after giving notice in writing. One inspection every three months is the norm, although other situations where an inspection can be carried out are specified (e.g. following a reportable accident).

Safety representatives can also inspect the scene of a reportable accident or dangerous occurrence.

Inspection of documents

Safety representatives can inspect any document which the employer has to maintain, other than documents relating to the health records of identifiable individuals.

Approved Code of Practice

Qualifications of safety representatives

So far as is reasonably practicable, safety representatives should have had two years' experience with the employer or in similar employment.

Functions of safety representatives

The following functions are specified:

1. They must keep themselves informed of legal requirements.

2. They must encourage cooperation between employer and employees.
3. They must carry out health and safety inspections and inform the employer of the outcome of these inspections.

Obligations of employers

Employers must provide information on:

1. the plans and performance of the undertaking with regard to health and safety at work;
2. the hazards and precautions necessary;
3. the occurrence of accidents, dangerous occurrences and occupational disease; and
4. any other information, including the results of any measurements taken, for instance, air monitoring, noise measurements.

Safety committees

The basic objectives of safety committees are to promote cooperation and act as a focus for employee participation. They have the following functions:

1. to consider the circumstances of individual accidents and cases of reportable diseases, and accident statistics and trends;
2. to examine safety audit reports;
3. to consider reports and information from the HSE;
4. to assist in the development of safety rules and systems;
5. to conduct periodic inspections;
6. to monitor the effectiveness of health and safety training, communications and publicity;
7. to provide a link with the Inspectorate.

Membership

Safety committees should be reasonably compact but allow for representation of management and all employees. Management representation can include line managers, supervisors, engineers, personnel specialists, medical and safety advisers.

To be effective, the committee must have authority to take action. Specialist knowledge should be made available to the committee.

Arrangements at individual workplaces

The following matters must be considered:

1. division of conduct of activities;
2. clear objectives and terms of reference of the committees;

3. the membership and structure of committee should be clearly defined in writing; and
4. arrangements must be made for publication of matters notified by safety representatives to the committee.

Meetings should be held as often as necessary, and agendas and minutes should be prepared.

Consultation with employees

The Health and Safety (Consultation with Employees) Regulations (HSCER) 1996 brought in changes to the law with regard to the health and safety consultation process between employers and employees.

Under the current Safety Representatives and Safety Committees Regulations (SRSCR) 1977, employers must consult safety representatives appointed by any trade unions they recognise.

Under the HSCER 1996 employers must consult any employees who are not covered by the SRSCR. This may be by direct consultation with employees or through representatives elected by the employees they are to represent

HSE Guidance

HSE Guidance accompanying the Regulations details:

1. which employees must be involved;
2. the information they must be provided with;
3. procedures for the election of representatives of employee safety (ROES);
4. the training, time off and facilities they must be provided with; and
5. their functions in office.

Risk assessment

Introduction

All modern protective legislation is based on the concept of risk assessment. The Management of Health and Safety at Work Regulations 1999 impose an absolute duty on employers to undertake a 'suitable and sufficient risk assessment' with respect to the risks to which their employees are exposed and to which non-employees may also be exposed as a result of the activities of the employer's undertaking. (See MANAGEMENT OF HEALTH AND SAFETY AT WORK REGULATIONS 1999.) Information on the risk assessment process is incorporated in the Approved Code of Practice to the regulations and in the HSE publication '5 Steps to Risk Assessment'.

The risk assessment process

A risk assessment is essentially a four-stage process:

1. identification of all the hazards;
2. measurement of the risks;
3. evaluation of the risks; and
4. implementation of measures to eliminate or control the risks.

There are different approaches and these can be adopted in the workplace, e.g.:

1. examination of each activity which could cause injury;
2. examination of hazards and risks in groups, e.g. machinery, substances, transport; and/or
3. examination of specific departments, sections, offices, construction sites.

In order to be suitable and sufficient and to comply with legal requirements, a risk assessment must:

1. identify all the hazards associated with the operation and evaluate the risks arising from those hazards, taking into account current legal requirements;
2. record the significant findings if more than five persons are employed, even if they work in different locations;

3. identify any group of employees, or single employees as the case may be, who are especially at risk;
4. identify others who may be specially at risk (e.g. visitors, contractors, members of the public);
5. evaluate existing controls, stating whether or not they are satisfactory and, if not, what action should be taken;
6. evaluate the need for information, instruction, training and supervision;
7. judge and record the probability or likelihood of an accident occurring as a result of uncontrolled risk;
8. record any circumstances arising from the assessment where serious and imminent danger could arise; and
9. provide an action plan giving information on implementation of additional controls, in order of priority, and with a realistic timescale.

Recording the assessment

The assessment must be recorded where more than five persons are employed.

Generic assessments

These are assessments produced once only for a given activity or type of workplace. Where an organisation has several locations or situations where the same activity is undertaken a generic risk assessment can be carried out for a specific activity to cover all locations. Similarly, where operators work away from the main location and undertake a specific task (e.g. installation of telephones or servicing of equipment), a generic assessment should be produced.

Maintaining the risk assessment

The risk assessment must be maintained. This means that any significant change to a workplace, process or activity, or the introduction of any new process, activity or operation, should be subject to risk assessment. If new hazards come to light, then these should also be subject to risk assessment.

The risk assessment should be reviewed and updated periodically. This is best achieved by a suitable combination of safety inspection and monitoring techniques, which require corrective and/or additional action where the need is identified. The process for monitoring, review and corrective action for risk assessment is shown in Figure 16, pp. 164–5.

Reviewing the risk assessment

The frequency of review depends upon the level of risk in the operation, but should not normally exceed ten years. Further, if a serious accident occurs in the organisation, or elsewhere but is possible in the organisation, and where a check on the risk assessment shows no assessment or a gap in assessment procedures, then a review is necessary.

Risk/hazard control

Once the risk or hazard has been identified and assessed, employers must prevent the risk arising or control it. Much will depend upon the magnitude of the risk. In certain cases, the level of competence of operators may need to be assessed prior to their undertaking certain work.

Commonly occurring hazards

It may be necessary to consider the following hazards when undertaking risk assessments:

Fall of a person from a height	Fall of an object/material from a
Fall of a person on the same level	height
Use of work equipment	Manual handling
Fire	Operation of vehicles
Drowning	Electricity
Stored energy	Excavation work
Contact with hot/cold surfaces	Explosions
Mechanical lifting operations	Compressed air
Biological agents	Noise and vibration
Adverse weather	Radiation
Storage of goods	Hazardous substances
Temperature, lighting and	Housekeeping/cleaning
ventilation	

RISK ASSESSMENT FOR

Company Name _____

Company Address _____

_____

_____

Postcode

ASSESSMENT UNDERTAKEN

(date) _____

Signed _____

Date _____

ASSESSMENT REVIEW

Date _____

STEP 1

List significant hazards here.

STEP 2

List groups of people who are at risk from the significant hazards you have identified.

STEP 3

List existing controls or note where the information may be found. List risks which are not adequately controlled and the action needed.

STEP 1

Hazard

Look only for hazards which you could reasonably expect to result in significant harm under the conditions in your workplace. Use the following examples as a guide

- slipping/tripping hazards (eg poorly maintained floors or stairs)
- fire (eg from flammable materials)
- chemicals (eg battery acid)
- moving parts of machinery (eg blades)
- work at height (eg from mezzanine floors)
- ejection of material (eg from plastic moulding)
- pressure systems (eg steam boilers)
- vehicles (eg fork-lift trucks)
- electricity (eg poor wiring)
- dust (eg from grinding)
- fumes (eg welding)
- manual handling
- noise
- poor lighting
- low temperatures

STEP 2

Who might be harmed?

There is no need to list individuals by name – just think about groups of people doing similar work or who may be affected, eg

- office staff
- maintenance personnel
- contractors
- people sharing your workplace
- operators
- cleaners
- members of the public

Pay particular attention to:

- staff with disabilities
- visitors
- inexperienced staff
- lone workers

They may be more vulnerable.

STEP 3

Is more needed to control the risk?

For the hazards listed, do the precautions already taken:

- meet the standards set by a legal requirement?
- comply with a recognised industry standard?
- represent good practice?
- reduce risk as far as reasonably practicable?

Have you provided:

- adequate information, instruction or training?
- adequate systems or procedures?

If so, then the risks are adequately controlled, but you need to indicate the precautions you have in place. (You may refer to procedures, company rules, etc.)

Where the risk is not adequately controlled, indicate what more you need to do (the 'action list')

STEP 5

Review and revision

Set a date for the review of the assessment (see opposite)

On review check that the precautions for each hazard still adequately control the risk. If not indicate the action needed.

Note the outcome. If necessary complete a new page for the risk assessment.

Making changes in your workplace, eg when bringing in new

- machines
- substances
- procedures

may introduce new hazards. Look for them and follow the 5 steps.

Figure 16 Health and Safety Executive risk assessment document (Source: HSE (1999) *Five Steps to Risk Assessment*, HMSO, London.)

Statements of health and safety policy

Introduction

Under section 2(3) of the Health and Safety at Work etc. Act 1974 (HSWA) every employer has a duty to 'prepare and as often as appropriate revise a written statement of his general policy with respect to the health and safety at work of his employees and the organisation and arrangements for the time being in force for carrying out that policy, and to bring the statement and any revision of it to the notice of his employees'.

The Statement of Health and Safety Policy is the key document for detailing the management systems and procedures to ensure sound levels of health and safety performance. It should be revised at regular intervals. This entry comprises a specimen Statement of Health and Safety Policy.

Specimen statement of health and safety policy

STATEMENT OF HEALTH AND SAFETY POLICY

HEALTH AND SAFETY AT WORK etc. ACT 1974

Part 1

Statement of Intent

1. It is the policy of this company to take all measures which are reasonably practicable to:
    (a) ensure the health, safety and welfare of all persons at work; and
    (b) protect visitors to the premises and the public generally against risks to their health and safety which may arise from this company's activities.

Management hereby undertake to provide the necessary resources and seek the cooperation of all employees with a view to implementing the requirements of the Health and Safety at Work etc. Act 1974 and other health and safety legislation shown at Appendix A.

The Managing Director has the general responsibility for implementing this Policy.

2. Management undertake, so far as is reasonably practicable:
    (a) to provide and maintain plant and systems of work that are safe and without risks to health;
    (b) to arrange for ensuring safety and the absence of risks to health in connection with the use, handling, storage and transport of articles and substances;
    (c) to provide such information, instruction, training and supervision as is necessary to ensure the health and safety at work of all persons at work;
    (d) to maintain all places of work in a condition that is safe and without risks to health, including the means of access to and egress from such places of work;
    (e) to provide and maintain a working environment for persons at work that is safe and without risks to health, with adequate arrangements for the welfare of such persons;
    (f) to define the responsibilities for all persons at work;
    (g) to promote joint consultation and employee involvement in health and safety at work;
    (h) to identify any hazards which may exist and bring the attention of such hazards and the precautions necessary to the attention of persons at work;
    (i) to record and investigate accidents and cases of occupational ill-health;
    (j) to monitor health and safety performance on a regular basis;
    (k) to provide and maintain appropriate personal protective equipment where necessary: and
    (l) to review this Statement of Health and Safety Policy as may be necessary.

All persons at work
In this Statement of Health and Safety Policy, 'all persons at work' includes managers and employees, the staff of contractors and sub-contractors, and other persons visiting the premises.

Part 2

Organisation and Arrangements for Implementing this Statement of Health and Safety Policy

1. Individual responsibilities

The Managing Director has ultimate responsibility for the health and safety at work of all persons at work on site. Senior managers and supervisors have responsibility for ensuring the health and safety at work of persons at work in their departments or sections respectively. These responsibilities, together with the chain of responsibility, are shown at Appendix B to this Statement.

2. Legal requirements

The Managing Director and line managers/supervisors will take all necessary measures to ensure compliance by the company with legal requirements and duties. They will also take into account Approved Codes of Practice and other forms of guidance published by the Health and Safety Commission and Health and Safety Executive, implementing such guidance so far as is reasonably practicable. The Safety Adviser will be consulted where there is a need for clarification of legal requirements and duties.

3. Health and safety instruction and training

The Managing Director, in conjunction with the Safety Adviser, is responsible for the identification of general and specific health and safety instruction and training needs of all persons at work on the site.

Health and safety training of persons at work will take place on induction, and where they may be exposed to new or increased risks through transfer or change of responsibilities, the introduction of new work equipment or a change respecting existing work equipment, the introduction of new technology, or the introduction of a new system of work or a change respecting an existing system of work.

4. Health and safety information

The Managing Director, in conjunction with the Safety Adviser, will ensure the dissemination of appropriate health and safety information to persons at work on the site. Facilities will be provided in the premises whereby the relevant health and safety information can be acquired or read by such persons.

5. Joint consultation

The Company Secretary will ensure that there is an effective system for joint consultation with employees on health and safety-related issues.

6. Safe systems of work

Management recognise the need for formally developed and documented safe systems of work. Safe systems of work will be prepared and documented for those activities and jobs where there is a risk of injury or occupational ill-health. Documented safe systems of work will be made available to all persons at work on site, and will be incorporated in health and safety training of those concerned.

7. Health and safety monitoring

Health and safety monitoring procedures, including safety audits and other recognised forms of monitoring, will be undertaken by the Safety Adviser.

A formal procedure, whereby persons at work may report hazards in their work, will be maintained and implemented.

8. Accident and ill-health reporting, recording and investigation

The Safety Adviser will ensure there is an effective system for the reporting, recording and investigation of accidents, ill-health and sickness absence involving all persons at work in accordance with current legal requirements.

9. Welfare amenity previsions

Management will ensure that welfare amenity provisions, i.e. sanitation, hand washing, showering facilities, clothing storage, drinking water and facilities for taking meals, are properly maintained.

10. Health surveillance and first aid arrangements

The Safety Adviser will ensure there is an effective system for health surveillance of employees identified as being at risk as a result of their work, and for first aid treatment.

The names and locations of first aid staff are indicated at Reception.

11. Plant acquisition and project work

The Managing Director, in conjunction with the Safety Adviser, will ensure that all new plant, equipment and processes do not expose persons at work to risk of injury and/or ill-health.

All project work, including that undertaking by external contractors and subcontractors, will be supervised with a view to protecting persons at work from risk of injury/ill-health.

12. Emergency procedure

The Managing Director, in conjunction with the Safety Adviser, will ensure that there is a formally established procedure to cover major emergencies, such as a large or rapidly escalating fire.

13. Contractors' activities

The Managing Director, in conjunction with the Safety Adviser and line managers, will ensure that there is an effective procedure for regulating the activities of both large and small contracting activities on site.

14. Substances hazardous to health

Foremen will ensure, in conjunction with the Safety Adviser, that all substances hazardous to health are identified and controlled in such a way as to prevent risk of injury or ill-health to all persons at work during their use, handling and storage.

The Safety Adviser will ensure that sufficient information relating to the hazards and precautions necessary on the part of all persons at work is made available.

15. Security

The Managing Director, in conjunction with the Safety Adviser and foremen, will take all reasonably practicable measures to protect all persons at work and their property from acts of physical assault, vandalism, theft, arson or bomb attack.

16. Work equipment

The Managing Director, in conjunction with the Safety Adviser, will ensure there is a satisfactory system for monitoring the safety of existing work equipment, including the need for frequent examination, testing and maintenance of such equipment.

17. Fire protection

The Managing Director, in conjunction with the Safety Adviser, will ensure there is a satisfactory system for the protection of all persons at work in the event of fire.

18. Vulnerable persons

Management will make special provision to ensure that 'vulnerable' groups of staff, such as young persons, disabled persons, pregnant female staff, new employees and employees undertaking unfamiliar tasks, are adequately supervised so as to prevent, so far as is reasonably practicable, risk of injury or ill-health.

Managing Director   xxx Co. Limited

Date

APPENDICES TO THE
STATEMENT OF HEALTH AND SAFETY POLICY

Appendix A
Current Health and Safety Legislation
Affecting this Company

The following Statutes and Regulations apply to the work of this company:

(To comprise the list of statutes and regulations currently in force)

Appendix B
Individual Duties and Responsibilities for
Health and Safety at Work

1. Managing Director

The Managing Director will ensure that there is an effective Statement of Health and Safety Policy, will periodically assess its effectiveness and ensure that any necessary changes are made.

2. Line managers/supervisors

Line managers/supervisors are generally responsible for ensuring the maintenance of appropriate levels of health and safety at work in the areas under their control. In particular, they are responsible for:

(a) ensuring the effective implementation of this Statement of Health and Safety Policy;

(b) keeping themselves informed of the incidents and accidents occurring in the workplace or to employees whilst at work;

(c) monitoring the arrangements for the health and safety training of employees;

(d) ensuring the maintenance of safe machinery, equipment, working conditions and systems of work;

(e) monitoring procedures for the provision and maintenance of personal protective equipment for employees;

(f) ensuring the maintenance of welfare facilities, including first aid and fire protection procedures;

(g) ensuring systems for the reporting, recording and investigation of accidents and ill-health are maintained; and

(h) ensuring systems for effective joint consultation with employees on health and safety-related matters are maintained.

3. Employees

All employees are responsible for:

(a) taking reasonable care for the health and safety of themselves and of other persons who may be affected by their acts or omissions at work; and

(b) cooperating with their employer in order to enable him or her to comply with duties imposed by him or her under health and safety law.

No person shall intentionally or recklessly interfere with or misuse anything provided in the interests of health, safety and welfare in pursuance of legal requirements.

In particular, every employee is responsible for:

(a) using any safe system of work, machinery, equipment, dangerous substance, transport equipment, means of production or safety device provided to him or her by his or her employer in accordance both with any training which has been received by him or her and the instructions respecting that use which have been provided by the employer in compliance with legal requirements;

(b) informing the line manager or the Safety Adviser:
   (i) of any situation which represents a serious and immediate danger to health and safety; and
   (ii) of any matter which represents a shortcoming in the employer's protection arrangements for health and safety;

(c) using any personal protective equipment provided in accordance with any training in the use of that personal protective equipment which has been received and the instructions respecting the use which have been provided by the employer;

(d) taking all reasonable steps to ensure that personal protective equipment is returned to the accommodation provided for it after use;

(e) reporting any loss of or obvious defect in the personal protective equipment to the foreman; and

(f) making full and proper use of any system of work provided in compliance with any manual handling risk assessment carried out by the employer.

4. Safety Adviser

Reporting directly to the Managing Director, the Safety Adviser is responsible for ensuring the provision of advice to the Managing Director, line managers and employees on all matters relating to the health, safety and welfare of employees, visitors to company locations and contractors on company locations.

In particular, he or she is responsible for:

(a) ensuring legal compliance by the company in all matters relating to health and safety at work;

(b) ensuring compliance by management and employees with their duties and responsibilities detailed in this Statement of Health and Safety Policy;

(c) the preparation of in-company codes of practice, instructions to employees and others, working procedures and safe systems of work;

(d) analysis of data relating to accidents and ill-health, including damage accidents and scheduled dangerous occurrences;

(e) carrying out risk assessments, safety audits, surveys and inspections of company premises;

(f) evaluating and examining new and existing work equipment, systems of work and operating procedures;

(g) liaising with occupational health personnel in respect of cases of occupational disease, ill-health and sickness absence;

(h) the identification, measurement, evaluation and control of airborne contaminants, noise and other health-related risks, such as those associated with manual handling operations;

(i) organising and running staff health and safety training activities; and

(j) liaison with officers of the enforcement authorities and safety organisations.

Appendix C
Hazards and Precautions

The following hazards, and the precautions necessary, are drawn to the attention of all employees:

Hazards   Precautions

(To comprise an appropriate list of hazards and precautions)

Structural safety

Introduction

Accidents associated with structural features of workplaces are common. These may include slips, trips and falls on the same level, falls down staircases, contact with structural features and glazed panels. The design of traffic routes must also be considered with particular attention paid to the segregation of pedestrians and vehicles using traffic routes. Specific requirements for ensuring structural safety are outlined in the Workplace (Health, Safety and Welfare) Regulations (WHSWR) 1992 and the HSC Approved Code of Practice accompanying these regulations.

Floors and traffic routes

All floors and the surfaces of traffic routes must be of suitable construction, free from dangerous holes, slopes and uneven and slippery surfaces, and provided with effective means of drainage where necessary. So far as is reasonably practicable, they must be kept free from obstruction and from articles and substances which could cause slips, trips or falls. Floors should be of sound construction, free from obstruction and sudden changes in level, and of non-slip finish. Where safety levels, production or the storage of goods are materially assisted, storage areas should be clearly marked by the use of yellow or white lines. 'No Go' areas should be cross-hatched with yellow lines. All openings in floors or significant differences in floor level should be fenced. Attention should also be paid to ensuring that floor loading does not produce structural instability.

Where a wet process is carried out, or where frequent floor washing is necessary, the floor should be laid to a fall to a drainage system. Floor channels, incorporating metal gratings or covers, can sometimes be used as an alternative.

Stairs, ladders and catwalks

Suitable and sufficient handrails and, if appropriate, guards must be provided on all traffic routes which are staircases except in circumstances in which a handrail cannot be provided without obstructing the traffic route. In the case of very wide staircases, further handrails may be necessary in addition to those at the sides. If necessary, the space between the handrail and the treads should be filled in, or an intermediate rail fitted.

Fixed vertical ladders and catwalks, including bridges to them, should be securely fixed. Where practicable, back rings should be fitted to vertical ladders from a height of 2 metres upwards and spaced at 1 metre intervals. Catwalks and bridges should be adequately fenced by means of 1 metre high guard rails, 500 mm high intermediate rails and toe boards.

External areas, traffic routes and approach roads

Under the WHSWR there is a general requirement that every workplace shall be organised in such a way that pedestrians and vehicles can circulate in a safe manner. A traffic route is defined as meaning a route for pedestrian traffic, vehicles or both and includes any stairs, staircase, fixed ladder, doorway, gateway, loading bay or ramp.

Traffic routes must be suitable for the persons or vehicles using same, sufficient in number, in suitable positions and of sufficient size. Particular precautions must be taken to prevent pedestrians or vehicles causing danger to persons near that route, ensure there is sufficient separation of traffic routes for vehicles from doors, gates and pedestrian routes, and where pedestrians and vehicles use the same traffic routes, ensure there is sufficient separation between them. Traffic routes must be suitably indicated where necessary for reasons of health and safety.

To facilitate access to and egress from the workplace by people and vehicles, external areas should have impervious and even surfaces and be adequately drained to a drainage system. The provision of water supply points and hoses, for washing down yards and approaches, is recommended.

Windows, doors, gates and walls, etc.

Specific provisions relating to structural items such as windows, doors, gates, walls, skylights and ventilators are incorporated in the WHSWR thus:

1. Every window or other transparent or translucent surface in a wall or partition and every transparent or translucent surface in a door, gate or wall shall, where necessary for reasons of health and safety:
   (a) be of safety material or be protected against breakage; and
   (b) be appropriately marked or incorporate features so as, in either case, to make it apparent.
2. No window, skylight or ventilator which is capable of being opened shall be likely to be opened, closed or adjusted in a manner which

exposes any person performing such operations to a risk to his health or safety No window, skylight or ventilator shall be in a position to expose any person in the workplace to a risk to his health or safety.

3. All windows and skylights in a workplace shall be of a design or so constructed that they may be cleaned safely. In considering whether a window or skylight is safe, account may be taken of any equipment used in conjunction with the window or skylight or of devices fitted to the building.

4. Doors and gates shall be suitably constructed (including fitted with any necessary safety devices). Specific safety provisions apply to sliding doors/gates, powered doors and doors/gates which are capable of being opened by being pushed from either side. Thus:

   (a) any sliding door or gate must be fitted with a device to prevent it coming off its track during use;

   (b) any upward opening door or gate must be fitted with a device to prevent it falling back;

   (c) any powered door or gate must incorporate suitable and effective features to prevent it causing injury by trapping any person;

   (d) where necessary for reasons of health or safety, any powered door or gate must be capable of being operated manually unless it opens automatically if the power fails; and

   (e) any door or gate which is capable of opening by being pushed from either side must be of such a construction as to provide, when closed, a clear view of the space close to both sides.

5. Interior walls have a contribution to make to illuminance levels, colour schemes, the maintenance of physical cleanliness, sound insulation and the prevention of fire spread. They should be substantial, durable, smooth, easily cleaned and reflect light.

6. Ceilings and inner roof surfaces of workrooms should also assist in the maintenance of appropriate illuminance levels, heat insulation, sound insulation and physical cleanliness. Ceiling heights should be a minimum of 2.4 metres.

Escalators and moving walkways

The WHSWR makes special provisions for escalators and moving walkways. In both cases, they shall:

1. function safely;
2. be equipped with any necessary safety devices; and
3. be fitted with one or more emergency stop controls which are easily identifiable and readily accessible.

Work equipment

Introduction

Work equipment entails a broad range of equipment from sophisticated computer-driven manufacturing processes to simple hand tools, such as power drills and hammers. As such, the use of work equipment is a significant contributory factor in injuries at work, resulting in death and major incapacitating injuries such as amputations of limbs, blinding, fractures, serious burns and scalding.

Current requirements are incorporated in the Provision and Use of Work Equipment Regulations 1998 (PUWER) and more specific regulations such as the Lifting Operations and Lifting Equipment Regulations 1998 (LOLER). Under PUWER, employers are required to assess the risks associated with work equipment and either eliminate or control them. A risk assessment should take into account:

1. design features of the machine – the form and distribution of harm;
2. persons at risk – operator, supervisor, third parties – general circumstances of operation; and
3. specific events leading to injury.

Machinery hazards

The following hazards need to be considered:

1. traps;
2. entanglement of hair, clothing, jewellery and limbs in revolving shafts, line shafts, chucks, drills;
3. ejection of particles from a machine, e.g. abrasive wheels, disintegration of swarf on a lathe;
4. contact with a machine.

Specific events leading to injury

Typical events include:

1. unexpected start-up or movement;

2. reaching into a feed device;
3. uncovenanted stroke by a machine; and
4. machine failure.

Safety mechanisms

The detailed design of the mechanism controls the safety of the operator. Any consideration of safety mechanisms should include the following objectives and requirements:

Reliability

Given the conditions a component is subjected to over a period of time, it must perform in a reliable way. Warning systems must also be reliable to the extent that they operate for the purposes for which they were designed, and should be reliable when exposed to oil, vibration, shock, water, etc.

Precise operation

The mechanism should operate positively, e.g. precise linkage between rams and guards. The transmission angle on linkages must be minimal and control over wear on linkages is essential.

Protection against operator abuse and misuse

Abuse is associated with the operator trying to open the guard before it is due to open causing wear and as a result of harsh treatment. Misuse, on the other hand, is a calculated attempt to override the safety mechanism. Mechanisms must, therefore, be designed to prevent both abuse and misuse.

Fail-safe

When the component fails, it must do so in such a way that the machine stops and the guards stay closed, and not vice versa. This cannot always be achieved.

Correct method of assembly

Correct assembly of the safety mechanism is vital.

Provision and Use of Work Equipment Regulations 1998 (PUWER)

Work equipment as defined means any machinery, appliance, apparatus or tool and any assembly of components which, in order to achieve a common end, are arranged and controlled so that they function as a whole. Use in relation to work equipment is defined as 'any activity involving work equipment and includes starting, stopping, programming, setting, transporting, repairing, modifying, maintaining, servicing and cleaning'.

The principal duties on employers are:

1. To ensure that work equipment is so constructed or adapted as to be suitable for the purpose for which it is used or provided, taking into account working conditions and the risks to health and safety of persons which exist in the premises (Regulation 5).
2. To ensure work equipment is maintained in an efficient state, efficient working order and in good repair (Regulation 6).
3. Where there may be a specific risk from work equipment, to ensure use is restricted to persons given the task of using it, and any repairs, modifications, maintenance or servicing is restricted to specifically designated persons (Regulation 7).
4. To ensure that people who use thc equipment and anyone who supervises or manages such use has adequate information and, where appropriate, written instructions pertaining to the use of that work equipment (Regulation 8).
5. To ensure that people who use the equipment and anyone who supervises or manages such use has received adequate training in the methods which may be adopted when using it, any risks which such use may entail and the precautions to be taken (Regulation 9).
6. To ensure specific measures are taken with respect to dangerous parts of machinery (Regulation 10).
7. To take measures to ensure that the exposure of a person using work equipment to any risk to his or her health or safety from any hazard (specified below) is either prevented or, where not reasonably practicable, adequately controlled.

    The measures referred to above shall:

    (a) be measures other than the provision of PERSONAL PROTECTIVE EQUIPMENT (PPE) or of INFORMATION, instruction, TRAINING and supervision, so far as is reasonably practicable; and
    (b) include, where appropriate, measures to minimise the effects of the hazard as well as reduce the likelihood of the hazard occurring.

    The hazards referred to above are:

    (a) any article or substance falling or being ejected from work equipment;
    (b) rupture or disintegration of parts of work equipment;
    (c) work equipment catching fire or overheating;
    (d) the unintended or premature discharge of any article or of any gas,

dust, liquid, vapour or other substance which, in each case, is produced, used or stored in the work equipment; and

(e) the unintended or premature explosion of the work equipment or any article or substance produced, used or stored in it (Regulation 12).

8. To ensure that work equipment, parts thereof, and any article or substance produced, used or stored in same which, in each case, is at a high or very low temperature shall have protection where appropriate so as to prevent injury to any person by burn, scald or sear (Regulation 13).

9. Regulations 1–18 require the provision of controls and certain arrangements 'where appropriate' by employers, namely:
   (a) controls for starting or making a significant change in operating conditions (Regulation 14);
   (b) stop controls (Regulation 15);
   (c) emergency stop controls (Regulation 16);
   (d) controls (generally) (Regulation 17);
   (e) control systems (generally) (Regulation 18).

10. To ensure that, where appropriate, work equipment is provided with suitable means to isolate it from all sources of energy, which must be clearly identifiable and readily accessible (Regulation 19).

11. To ensure that work equipment or any part of it is stabilised by clamping or otherwise when necessary for purposes of health or safety (Regulation 20).

12. To ensure suitable and sufficient lighting, which takes account of the operations to be carried out, is provided at any place where a person uses work equipment (Regulation 21).

13. To take appropriate measures to ensure that work equipment is so constructed or adapted that, so far as is reasonably practicable, maintenance operations which involve a risk to health or safety can be carried out while the work is shut down or, in other cases:
   (a) maintenance operations can be carried out without exposing the person carrying them out to a risk to his or her health or safety; or
   (b) appropriate measures can be taken for the protection of any person carrying out maintenance operations which involve a risk to his or her health or safety (Regulation 22).

14. To ensure that work equipment is marked in a clearly visible manner with any marking appropriate for reasons of health and safety (Regulation 23).

15. To ensure that work equipment incorporates any warnings or warning devices which are appropriate for reasons of health and safety. Warnings given by warning devices on work equipment shall not be appropriate unless they are unambiguous, easily perceived and easily understood (Regulation 24).

PUWER also incorporates specific provisions with regard to mobile work equipment, such as lift trucks and power presses.

Management systems

The management systems required to ensure compliance by employers with the mainly absolute duties under these Regulations are:

1. the assessment of risks at the selection stage of new work equipment;
2. on-going safety assessment of existing work equipment;
3. the implementation and operation of formally documented routine and planned maintenance systems, which incorporate specific safety measures;
4. designation of certain trained persons for certain specific risk activities;
5. the provision of information, instruction and training for staff using any form of work equipment, particularly aimed at young people;
6. provision of adequate and suitable guards and protection devices to prevent access to any dangerous part of machinery or to any rotating stock-bar, or to stop the movement of any dangerous part or rotating stock-bar, before any person enters a danger zone, i.e. any zone in or around machinery in which any person is exposed to a risk to health or safety from contact with a dangerous part of machinery or a rotating stock-bar;
7. a general duty to prevent exposure to specified hazards, or where this is not reasonably practicable, to provide adequate controls.

Formal (primary) sources

EU Directives

These are the EU's legislative instruments. Directives are legally binding on the governments of all member states, which must introduce national legislation, or use administrative procedures where applicable, to implement their requirements.

Acts of Parliament (Statutes)

Acts of Parliament can be innovatory (introducing new legislation) or consolidating (reinforcing, with modifications, existing law). Statutes empower the minister or secretary of state to make Regulations, e.g. the Health and Safety at Work etc. Act 1974 (HSWA) and the Factories Act 1961.

Regulations (Statutory instruments)

Regulations are more detailed than the related Act, which lays down the framework and objectives of the system.

Statutory Rules and Orders (SR & Os)

These are the earlier equivalent of Statutory Instruments. They ceased to be published in 1948, but many applicable to occupational health and safety are still in force (e.g. Chains, Ropes and Lifting Tackle (Register) Order 1938).

Approved Codes of Practice (ACOPs)

The Health and Safety Commission (HSC) is empowered to approve and issue Codes of Practice for the purpose of providing guidance on health and safety duties and other matters laid down in Statute or Regulations. A Code of Practice can be drawn up by the Commission or the Health and Safety Executive (HSE). In every case, however, the relevant government department, or other body, must be consulted, and approval of the secretary of state must be obtained. Any Code of Practice approved in this way is an ACOP.

Case law (common law)

Case law is an important source of information. It is derived from common law because over the years judges have formulated rules and principles of law as the cases occur for decision before the courts.

Case law is found in law reports, for example, the *All England Law Reports,* the *Industrial Cases Reports,* the current *Law Year Book* and in professional journals, e.g. *Law Society Gazette, Solicitors' Journal.* In addition, many newspapers carry daily law reports, e.g. *The Times, Financial Times, Daily Telegraph* and *Independent.*

Non-legal sources

A wide range of non-legal sources of information are available, some of which may be quoted in legal situations.

HSE series of Guidance Notes

Guidance Notes issued by the HSE have no legal status. They are issued on a purely advisory basis to provide guidance on good health and safety practices, specific hazards, etc. There are five series of Guidance Notes: General, Chemical Safety, Plant and Machinery, Medical and Environmental Hygiene. See below for HSE details.

British Standards (BSs)

These are produced by the British Standards Institute. They provide guidance on numerous issues and are frequently referred to by enforcement officers as the correct way of complying with a legal duty.

Manufacturers' information and instructions

Under section 6 of the HSWA (as amended by the Consumer Protection Act 1987) manufacturers, designers, importers and installers of 'articles and substances used at work' have a duty to provide information relating to the safe use, storage, etc. of their products.

Safety organisations

Safety organisations (e.g. the Royal Society for the Prevention of Accidents (RoSPA) and the British Safety Council) provide information in the form of magazines, booklets and videos on a wide range of health and safety-related topics.

Professional institutions

Many professional institutions, such as the Institute of Occupational Safety and Health (IOSH), the Chartered Institute of Environmental Health (CIEH) and the British Occupational Hygiene Society (BOHS), provide information, both verbally and in written form.

Published information

This takes the form of textbooks, magazines, law reports, updating services, microfiche systems, films and videos on general and specific topics.

Internal sources

There are many sources of information available within organisations. These include:

Existing written information

This may take the form of STATEMENTS OF HEALTH AND SAFETY POLICY, company Health and Safety Codes of Practice, and specific company policies.

Company documentation may be presented in a court as an indication of the organisation's intention to regulate activities in order to ensure legal compliance. Evidence of the use of such information in staff training is essential here.

Work study techniques

Included here are the results of activity sampling, surveys, method study, work measurement and process flows.

Job descriptions

A job description should incorporate health and safety responsibilities and accountabilities. Compliance with health and safety requirements is an implied condition of every employment contract, breach of which may result in dismissal or disciplinary action by the employer.

Accident statistics

Statistical information on past accidents and sickness may identify unsatisfactory trends in operating procedures which can be eliminated at the design stage of safe systems of work.

The use of accident statistics and rates (e.g. accident incidence rate) as a sole measure of safety performance is not recommended however, owing to the variable levels of accident reporting. Under-reporting, common in many organisations, can result in inaccurate comparisons being made between one location and another.

Task analysis

Information produced by the analysis of tasks must be taken into account.

Job safety analysis, a development of task analysis, will provide the above information prior to the development of safe systems of work.

Direct observation

Direct observation identifies interrelationships between operators, hazards, dangerous practices and situations, and potential risk situations. It is an important source of information in ascertaining whether, for instance, formally designed safe systems of work are being operated, or safety practices, imparted as part of former training activities, are being followed.

Personal experience

The experience of accident victims, frequently recorded in accident reports, are an important source of information. Feedback from accidents is crucial in order to prevent repetition of these accidents.

Incident recall

This is a technique used in a damage control programme to gain information about near miss accidents.

Product complaints

A record of all product complaints and action taken should be maintained. Such information provides useful feedback in the modification of products and in the design of new products. Product complaints may also result in action by the enforcement authorities under section 6 of HSWA and/or civil proceedings in the event of injury, damage or loss sustained as a result of a defective product or defect in a product.

Bibliography and further reading

British Standards Institution (1996) *Guide to Occupational Health and Safety Management Systems (BS 8800)*, BSI, London

Confederation of British Industries (1991) *Developing a Safety Culture*, CBI, London

Department of Employment (1977) *Safety Representatives and Safety Committees Regulations 1977* (SI 1977: No. 500), HMSO, London

Department of Employment (1999) *Control of Substances Hazardous to Health Regulations 1999* SI 1999: No. 743), HMSO, London

Department of Employment (1994) *Chemicals (Hazard Information and Packaging for Supply) Regulations 1994* SI 1994: No. 3247), HMSO, London

Health and Safety Commission (2000) *Management of Health and Safety at Work: Approved Code of Practice: Management of Health and Safety at Work Regulations 1999*, HSE Books, London

Health and Safety Commission (1992) *Workplace Health, Safety and Welfare: Approved Code of Practice: Workplace (Health, Safety and Welfare) Regulations 1992*, HSE Books, London

Health and Safety Commission (1995) *Managing Construction for Health and Safety: Construction (Design and Management) Regulations 1994: Approved Code of Practice*, HSE Books, London

Health and Safety Commission (1995) *A Guide to Managing Health and Safety in Construction: Construction Industry Advisory Committee*, HSE Books, London

Health and Safety Commission (1995) *Designing for Health and Safety in Construction: Construction Industry Advisory Committee*, HSE Books, London

Health and Safety Executive (1980) *Effective Policies for Health and Safety*, HSE Books, London

Health and Safety Executive (1999) *Health and Safety Law: What You Should Know*, HMSO, London

Health and Safety Executive (1989) *Safe Systems of Work*, HSE Information Centre, Sheffield

Health and Safety Executive (1989) *Our Health and Safety Policy Statement: Writing your health and safety policy statement: Guide to preparing a safety policy statement for small businesses*, HMSO, London

189

Health and Safety Executive (1989) *Human Factors and Industrial Safety: Guidance Booklet HS(G)48*, HMSO, London

Health and Safety Executive (1989) *Memorandum of Guidance on the Electricity at Work Regulations 1989*, HMSO, London

Health and Safety Executive (1990) *A Guide to the Health and Safety at Work etc. Act 1974: Guidance on the Act*, HMSO, London

Health and Safety Executive (1991) *Successful Health and Safety Management*, HMSO, London

Health and Safety Executive (1992) *Personal Protective Equipment at Work: Guidance on the Personal Protective Equipment at Work Regulations 1992*, HMSO, London

Health and Safety Executive (1992) *Manual Handling: Guidance on the Manual Handling Operations Regulations 1992*, HMSO, London

Health and Safety Executive (1992) *Display Screen Equipment: Guidance on Regulations: Health and Safety (Display Screen Equipment) Regulations 1992*, HSE Books, London

Health and Safety Executive (1998) *Work Equipment: Guidance on Regulations: Provision and use of Work Equipment Regulations 1998*, HSE Books, London

Health and Safety Executive (1993) *Getting to Grips with Manual Handling*, HSE Information Centre, Sheffield

Health and Safety Executive (1995) *A Guide to Managing Health and Safety in Construction*, HSE Books, London

Health and Safety Executive (1995) *Health and Safety for Small Construction Sites*, HSE Books, London

Health and Safety Executive (1996) *The Reporting of Injuries, Diseases and Dangerous Occurrences*, HSE Information Centre, Sheffield

Health and Safety Executive (1996) *Guide to the Reporting of Injuries, Diseases and Dangerous Occurrences Regulations 1995*, HMSO, London

Health and Safety Executive (1996) *Health and Safety in Construction*, HSE Books, London

Health and Safety Executive (1998) *5 Steps to Risk Assessment*, HSE Information Centre, Sheffield

Stranks, J. (1994) *Human Factors and Safety*, Pitman Publishing, London

Stranks, J. (1994) *Management Systems for Safety*, Pitman Publishing, London

Stranks, J. (1995) *Occupational Health and Hygiene*, Pitman Publishing, London

Stranks, J. (1996) *Safety Technology*, Pitman Publishing, London

Stranks, J. (1996) *The Law and Practice of Risk Assessment*, Pitman Publishing, London

Stranks, J. (1997) *A Manager's Guide to Health and Safety at Work*, Kogan Page, London

Stranks, J. (1999) *Health and Safety Law*, FT Pitman Publishing, London
Stranks, J. (2000) *Handbook of Health and Safety Practice*, FT Pitman
    Publishing, London

Useful Addresses

Health and Safety Executive

Information Centres

Baynards House	Broad Lane
1 Chepstow Place	Sheffield
Westbourne Grove	S3 7HQ
London W2 4TF	

Tel 020 7221 0870	Tel 0114 2912300
FAX 020 7221 9178	
Website: www.hse.gov.uk	

HSE Books
PO Box 1999
Sudbury
Suffolk
CO10 6FS

Tel 01787 881165
FAX 01787 313995
Website: www.hsebooks.co.uk

Institution Of Occupational Safety and Health
The Grange
Highfield Drive
Wigston
Leicestershire
LE18 1NN

Tel 0116 257 3100
FAX 0116 257 3101
Website: http:/www.iosh.co.uk
e-mail: comms@iosh.co.uk

National Examination Board in Occupational Safety and Health
5 Dominus Way
Meridian Business Park
Leicester
LE3 2QW

Tel 0116 263 4700
FAX 0116 282 4000
Website: www.nebosh.org.uk

Chartered Institute of Environmental Health

Chadwick Court
15 Hatfields
London
SE1 8DJ

Tel 020 7928 6006
FAX 020 7827 5866
Website: www.cieh.org.uk